JOHN DREBINGER
PRESENTATIONS

WOULD YOU WATCH OUT FOR MY SAFETY?

Helping Others Avoid Personal Injury

John W. Drebinger Jr., C.Ht., CSP
CERTIFIED SPEAKING PROFESSIONAL

First Edition

Wulamoc Publishing
Galt, California

WOULD YOU WATCH OUT FOR MY SAFETY?

Helping Others Avoid Personal Injury

By
John Warner Drebinger Jr., C.Ht., CSP

Published by:
Wulamoc Publishing
13541 Christensen Rd.
Galt, CA 95632 U.S.A.

Drebinger, John W., Jr., WOULD YOU WATCH OUT FOR MY SAFETY?: Helping Others Avoid Personal Injury by John Warner Drebinger Jr. 1st ed.
Includes bibliographical references.
ISBN 978-1-890296-05-6 (pbk)

Order Information

To order additional copies of this book (volume discounts available) or to receive information

Contact:

John Drebinger Presentations

Phone:
(209) 745-9419

Visit Our Website:

http://www.drebinger.com

E-Mail:

office@drebinger.com

Warning – Disclaimer

This book is designed to provide information on communication skills. It is sold with the understanding that the publisher and author are not engaged in rendering legal, accounting, or other professional services. The author, while an expert in communicating safety messages, holds the National Speakers Association's highest earned designation of Certified Speaking Professional, CSP, he is not a Certified Safety Professional, also coincidently using the initials CSP. If legal or other expert assistance is required, the services of a competent professional should be sought.

The purpose of this book is not to reprint all the information that is otherwise available to the authors and/or publisher, but to complement, amplify, and supplement other texts. You are urged to read all the available material to learn as much as possible about communicating safety, and to tailor the information to your individual needs. For more information, see the many references in the recommended reading list.

Safety is a serious subject and if you aren't sure about technical issues you should consult someone who is qualified to give you the right information.

Every effort has been made to make this book as complete and accurate as possible. However, there **may be mistakes,** both typographical and in content. Therefore, this text should be used only as a general guide and not as the ultimate source of information on this subject. Furthermore, this book contains information on communication skills only up to the printing date.

The purpose of this book is to educate and entertain. The author and Wulamoc Publishing shall have neither liability nor responsibility to any person or entity with respect to any loss or damage caused, or alleged to be caused, directly or indirectly by the information contained in this book.

If you do not wish to be bound by the above, you may return this book to the publisher for a full refund.

Industry Praise For This Book

John's presentations are wonderful! They are so varied that we are bringing him back to do another presentation. I am so excited about this book, that I am buying the first 500 copies so each of our employees will have their own copy. Great communication is one of the most crucial components of a positive Safety Culture! This book is just what we need to help give our employees the skills they need to "watch out for each other's safety" everyday! As usual, John, excellent work!

Jeremy J. Jones, Safety Manager
Peabody Energy - Twentymile Mine

The book is enjoyable and easy to read. You let the reader address his or her own responsibility to see something and to say something to protect their fellow workers, friends, family, and just people on the street. The insight you give will give anyone reading it a different outlook on safety. If we don't speak up, we all lose.

Pat Gagliardi
Senior Shop Steward
Safety Committee
IBEW Local Union #3
Con Edison Staten Island Division

I am impressed - great job. Starting with stories and then going into the meat of things is very effective. I could see a lot of what we try and do, however you bring it home.

Fred Hrenchir

I truly enjoyed the book and I believe it will keep many safe. You will never know how many people you will save from an incident.

Mack Wimbish
Quantum Safety Consulting Inc.,

Very well done. Telling a story gets the point across. Great job - thanks for sharing.

Powell T. Stevenson-CSHM, Four-Safety

Your book deals with events that we can all relate to in our daily lives. You held my interest and I do practice watching out for others safety.

Don Melanson
IUE Local 201
Elected Health and Safety Rep,
LAT & O, G.E.

John writes in a conversational and easy to read manner as he leads us on a journey that challenges us to consider our attitude toward our personal safety, and just as importantly, our attitude and willingness to take responsibility for the safety of others. A great reminder that safety isn't just something we do at work but something that should be a core value of who we are at home, at work and at play. Thank you, John, for your concern for others and the skill to give us practical tools to make a difference day by day.

Cliff Butler, Accurate Dispersions

This book has a great message. It's written in John's characteristic conversational, storytelling style. His approach is effective, personal, and reaches a wide variety of audiences. Thanks, John, for continuing to be a great ambassador for the safety profession.

Phillip A. Combest, CSP, ARM
Safety & Risk Management Professional

John Drebinger is one of the most dynamic and motivational speakers I have had the pleasure to listen to. John is an excellent writer and his latest book conveys the reasons people should watch out for each other's safety and in turn cause them to take action.

Harold R. Hobbs
Attorney-at-Law, The Hobbs Law Firm

Dedication

This book is dedicated to my good friend and inspiration, Dr. E. Scott Geller. There are thousands of people who have made it home safely every day because of the work Scott has done over the years. His dedication to sharing his wealth of knowledge with the rest of us has been a true blessing in my life.

Scott has a passion for life and helping others that is inspiring to everyone with whom he comes in contact.

He has selflessly spent hours helping me improve my presentations over the years. I appreciate that he has always been willing to listen to my ideas and give feedback that makes my presentations and my writing more effective. He has taught me research-based principles that help people work safely.

In addition to our professional relationship, I am blessed to be able to call Scott my friend. I cherish the time we have spent together in front of his fireplace, late into the night discussing life, football, politics and, of course, safety.

I should mention as one arrives at his house, there is a sign outside his beautiful property, "Make-A-DiffRanch". That is what his whole life is about - making a difference. I can assure you he has made a difference in the lives of thousands of people. His ideas and research have changed the face of the safety profession. He is someone who has truly made a difference in my life.

Iron sharpens iron, and one man sharpens another.
                                                    Proverbs 27:17

Where there is no counsel, the people fall; but in the multitude of counselors there is safety.
                                                    Proverbs 11:14

Table Of Contents

Introduction
How To Read This Book

This book is written in two different styles. The first five chapters are written in story form. All of the concepts are contained in the story. The second part of the book, beginning with Chapter Six, addresses the "why and how to" aspects of the subject. The same principles are explained in each section, so if you like a good story, start at Chapter One. If you want to cut to the straight training material, start with Chapter Six. Either way, it is said repetition is the mother of learning and that is designed into this practical book.

Thank you for taking the time to care enough about yourself, your family, your co-workers, and your friends to read this book. Also, I believe you should begin a book with useful content and for that reason the acknowledgements and other sections are at the end.

Do not look at things that are and say why, dream of things that aren't and say why not.

- Robert Kennedy

Chapter One

One Lucky Morning

It was 4:10 in the morning. Jeff and his wife, Karen, were rolling down a country road in their mini-van on their way to the airport, forty-five minutes away. Suddenly, as Jeff changes the radio, Karen sees a large shape in the road and screams out, "COW!"

Jeff looks up and it appears as if nothing is there. Then he spots it - a huge, black cow standing in the middle of his lane. By the grace of God, she had warned Jeff in time for him to easily slow down and avoid a collision. It's a good thing she was paying attention and was watching out for their safety. If he had been driving by himself that day, he surely would have hit that cow.

There's no question about it. A big mess was surely avoided. The airbag would have gone off and he never would have made it to his flight; what a hassle that would have been! Instead, since someone was watching out for Jeff's safety, he was blessed and they continued on to the airport with no harm done.

They arrive at the airport and say their goodbyes. Jeff checks his bags with his friend, Henry, and proceeds through security. He quickly forgets the close call he had experienced just a half hour before. He arrives at his gate, greeted by his favorite gate agent, Julie. As usual, Jeff is the first passenger on the plane. This is one of the privileges he enjoys most, due to his frequent-flyer status. He likes being first on the airplane because he can go to sleep quickly and be rested upon arrival at his destination.

Before falling off to sleep on the airplane, Jeff calls Karen to thank her for taking him to the airport so early in the morning. She replies, "No problem." Then she tells Jeff she had decided to take a different route home that morning.

"Why was that?" he asks.

She replies, "I was listening to the radio during the drive home and they said there was a big wreck." A large milk truck had run into a cow on Twin Cities Road — the same cow they had avoided earlier that morning. Fortunately, no one was injured except the cow.

Jeff comments, "I'm glad it was a big truck. I'm sure that's why the driver didn't get hurt." He says goodbye to Karen and ponders about what had happened.

Jeff realizes he had two close calls that morning. First, almost hitting the cow and second, someone could have been seriously injured or killed because he didn't report the hazard. He had not watched out for the safety of others. What was he thinking?

Well, he was driving in the countryside and people are supposed to be on the lookout for livestock. Yet, that didn't matter when he was approaching the cow. It was only because someone else was watching out for his safety that nothing bad happened to him. Unfortunately, he didn't do the same favor for the truck driver. He thinks for a moment, "What if that had been somebody taking their kid to school?"

Chapter Two

Discovering the Reasons

Jeff falls asleep on the plane before it has even taken off. With the roar of the jet engines in the background, he begins to dream. He is back on Twin Cities Road, but this time he is not driving; he is watching the cow he had avoided earlier that morning standing in the middle of the road.

He hears a voice advising him he was one of the lucky ones. "Lucky? How am I lucky?" he asks the voice. The answer is he was lucky a large truck hit the cow on the road.

Because he chose not to warn others of the hazard on the road, a collision occurred that could have been avoided. No one needed to be hurt and the fact a truck took the hit meant he had avoided a greater nightmare.

The voice asks him to imagine the consequences had it been a small car with a child passenger. What if that child had not been in a safety seat and upon colliding with the cow had been thrown out through the windshield of the car.

Horrified, he realizes he isn't just hearing the voice; he is actually there observing the event. No one can see or hear him, yet he can see and hear it all happen. It is like a 3-D holographic movie happening right in front of him.

There stands the cow and in the distance, Jeff sees a car approaching. Somehow, he sees a mother driving with her child in the front seat. The boy suddenly drops his iPod on the floor and he unfastens his safety belt to reach down for it. Mom is distracted by the interior light, which her son had turned on to find the missing iPod.

The mother looks ahead but due to the glare caused by the interior light and the fact the cow on the road was black, she doesn't see it as she approaches. Going just under the speed limit of fifty-five miles per hour on this country road, she sees the cow much too late to react.

The older-model car careens into the cow and the child is catapulted out through the window, sliding across the coarse asphalt. After a few bounces, the child comes to a motionless stop. Jeff races over to the child. He sees no signs of life. Helpless, he listens, not a groan could be heard, not a breath could be seen. The driver of the car slouches unconscious against the steering wheel that had stopped her forward motion. Minutes later, a highway patrolman who was on his way to work arrives. He calls for paramedics and begins to evaluate the situation.

Jeff yells impatiently to the voice, "You still haven't explained why you consider me lucky."

The voice answers, "You are lucky because the scene you just witnessed never happened. You are lucky a large milk truck hit the cow in the road when you chose not to report the hazard. You didn't watch out for other people's safety. All the bad that came out of that moment of not actively caring about others is a dead cow and a slightly damaged truck. Because the truck was big and the driver was buckled up, he was just fine."

"You don't have to live that nightmare over and over however; you need to understand how important it is for us to watch out for each other's safety. Until you learn the value of watching out for other's safety, I will cause you to experience unpleasant dreams to teach you what you need to know. For you, these are only dreams. For the people you will see injured, the nightmare never ends."

"Who are you?" Jeff asks.

The voice replies, "I have dedicated my life to helping people work safely. I have been doing this so long, it is as if my message of safety has been multiplied through thousands of others over the years. I suspect that is why you can hear me right now. It seems when the person is ready for it, my voice comes to them to help them understand."

"Do you have a name?" Jeff asks.

"Sure, my name is Joe." The voice responds.

Jeff replies, "Nice to meet you Joe, and thanks for caring about me and my family and so many people. I guess because you are here I must be ready to learn. So what's next?"

Joe transports Jeff to a new location and Jeff finds himself outside an office building. He observes people walking up a small flight of stairs past a young man who is scraping the old paint off a grating. He is a young painter's apprentice and he is working hard in the humid Houston heat.

In this dream, Jeff instantly knows information about the young painter's apprentice. Married a little over one year, he and his young wife have a baby daughter, Lauren, who had just been born two weeks ago. Lauren's mom, Jessica, had kissed her husband, Paul, that morning as he left for work. As Paul drove away, Jessica had no idea she may have kissed him for the last time.

As Jeff watches, he realizes he could actually hear people's thoughts as they walk by the young man. One person looks over, sees Paul, and thinks to himself, "I hope he turned the power off; there is electrical wiring under that grate."

The people walking by continue on their way not saying a word. Many others walked by not even noticing Paul, the young apprentice, and some who notice him are as unaware as he is of the potential danger so close to the tool he was using to scrape off old paint.

Over the next few minutes, Jeff becomes more and more tense with each and every scrape. One slip of the blade and Paul could be killed. Yet, Jeff has no power to tell him as he cannot be seen or heard. Only those who pass Paul on the stairs can make a difference in this case. Frustrated, Jeff tries to signal him but nothing works. Jeff then begins to attempt to influence the people who walk by. He hears the most common thought, "That guy must know there is electricity under there. Should I say something? No, I'm sure he is aware of it."

Jeff screams back, "Of course you should say something! He has no idea!"

Then suddenly, it happens. The blade of Paul's paint scraper slips through the grating and a huge arc of electricity can be seen and heard. Sparks fly and he falls backward lying on the ground. Jeff helplessly watches in horror! He is sure Paul has been killed. After a few moments that seem like forever, Paul sits up. Dazed and cautious, the young man brushes himself off.

Several of Paul's fellow workers arrive on the scene. They ask him what happened and he answers he doesn't know.

It turns out the people who passed by seeing the hazard, but choosing not to watch out for his safety, are as lucky as Jeff. Over the next few days, they come forward during the analysis of the incident and state they had seen Paul but assumed he was aware of the risk or the power must have been turned off.

Jeff wonders if they would now have dreams similar to his

because of failure to actively care. They had been extremely lucky. Had that young man been killed, Jeff is sure they wouldn't have come forward because they wouldn't want anyone to know how they had let him down. They would be haunted by the truth that they noticed the hazard, but chose to say nothing. For the rest of their lives, they would know a young man with a family had died because they failed to watch out for his safety. They had been saved from the nightmares that would have kept them from peaceful sleep for many nights to come. They were indeed blessed it all worked out okay.

Jeff asks Joe if anyone would be visiting them to teach them how important it is to make sure to always watch out for other people's safety. Joe comments, "It could be me or the voice of some other dedicated safety person."

As quickly as this dream began, it's over. Jeff is awakened as the flight attendants are serving breakfast. He says grace and enjoys his usual fruit plate. The flight attendants always make sure he has fruit as Julie, the gate agent, usually brags about Jeff's accomplishment of burning off more than one hundred pounds of fat. He did this by riding a bike six miles a day and eating more like his fit friends.

As Jeff eats, he ponders the dream he just experienced. He usually remembers his dreams and he makes a note to write this one down in his journal. He wishes he could call Karen to tell her about the dream. Soon after he finishes breakfast, he drifts back into a deep sleep.

He finds himself with Joe at the substation of a major utility company in the Midwest. This substation has three people working in it. One of them, named Bob, has been with the company for over five years. The other two have been with the company for only two years. These two newer workers are on the floor of the substation, cleaning. Above them, on a ladder, Bob is cleaning a wall. Near him is a high-voltage bus, of which he is unaware.

His two fellow workers know it is there, yet they choose not to say anything about it to Bob. Why? Don't they care about his safety? As Jeff listens to their thoughts, he hears one of them think, "Bob has been doing this job longer than I have; I'm sure he knows what he is doing."

The other worker thinks, "Bob's awfully close to the bus but who am I to tell him what to do? After all, he must know it's there. I don't want to insult his common sense."

This whole experience is so strange. Somehow, Jeff knew that Bob didn't know about the electrical hazard. In fact, Bob had never been at this particular substation before, nor had he ever been in one with the same floor plan. He had no idea he was so close to a deadly hazard that could end his life in an instant. Once again, Jeff knows what people are thinking, yet is unable to alter the events as they unfold.

Transported back in time to earlier that morning, Jeff can see and hear Bob with his wife, Evelyn, and their daughter, Kelly. At breakfast, Kelly was excitedly telling him about how great it was to finally be a senior in high school. She had been elected class president and it was hard to imagine things being better. Bob's wife worked at the high school as a counselor and after Bob left for work, Kelly and Evelyn hopped into their car and off they went. Neither of them gave a thought their lives could change in a second.

Suddenly, Jeff is back in the substation and watches as Bob moves closer to the bus. Once again, Jeff screams out but no one can hear him.

As Jeff looks over at Bob, he sees a flash of light. The electricity arcs and grounds out right through Bob. He slides down the ladder, limp and lifeless. The awful smell of an electrical burn quickly fills the air. His two fellow workers look up and see him falling to the ground. They use a non-conducting tool to pull him away from the ladder.

Once they are sure they can safely do so, they check to see if Bob is alive. Miraculously, he is. As they turn him over, they see the massive damage the voltage has caused as it blew out of his left hand searching out the closest ground. One of them quickly calls for help on his cellular phone.

Help arrives quickly and Bob is rushed to the hospital. His wife, Evelyn, is called at the school and told the bad news. She puts the phone down, tells someone she has an emergency and must leave. Quickly, she goes to her daughter's classroom and asks her to join her in the hall.

Kelly sees the look of concern in Mom's eyes. "What is going on?" she asks. Her mom tells her Dad has been injured at work and is at the hospital. Silently, they rush to the car and drive across the small town to the hospital.

When they arrive, they are met by some of Bob's co-workers who have begun a vigil, waiting and praying for his survival. The medical team informs her of his condition, which is critical. All they can do now is wait.

After what seems like an eternity, Evelyn is allowed to see Bob. She steels herself to stay positive, no matter what. She knows she has to put on an optimistic front for Bob's sake. The damage is extensive, yet he is lucky he hasn't been killed. Unfortunately, the electrical burns destroyed so much tissue that, even with outstanding medical care, he had to have his right arm amputated. The doctors worked miracles on his left arm, saving just enough muscle tissue to enable him to keep it. He improves in the days to come and is told he will need extensive physical therapy to recover any use of his remaining arm.

Unfortunately, the town in which they live and work doesn't

have facilities for this kind of treatment, so the family makes the difficult choice for Bob to live in a different city. By not moving the whole family, Kelly can complete her senior year as class president of her high school. Once a month, they visit Bob.

Over the year, his therapists work miracles. After all the physical therapy, things improve and Bob returns home to begin his new life with the injury he sustained. As for Bob's two fellow workers, the psychological pain they experienced will never go away. For the rest of their lives, they will be haunted with the realization they allowed Bob to be injured.

Because they didn't watch out for Bob's safety, they would suffer the nightmare over and over again. The only saving grace is that Bob survived and they don't have to face his widow and fatherless daughter. Jeff begins to realize Joe was right; he has been blessed the whole incident with the cow worked out the way it did.

After these dreams, Jeff finds himself talking to Joe again. Joe asks him if he feels differently about watching out for other people's safety.

"You bet," Jeff answers. "In fact, with each succeeding dream I found it more and more frustrating I wasn't able to say something to help someone avoid an injury. It's frustrating to know people saw the hazard or the risky behavior and, while they could easily say something, they chose not to."

Jeff asks himself what he could do to help people realize the value in watching out for each other's safety. He also wonders why people don't just do so naturally.

Joe answers, "That is the biggest part of the problem; people don't have a big enough reason WHY they should watch out for each other's safety. People will do whatever they need to if they have a good enough reason why they should."

Jeff responds, "I wish I could give people a convincing reason why they need to watch out for others' safety." "Good news," Joe answers. "I can share five reasons with you and then you can spread the word."

"Great, let's get started," Jeff replies excitedly.

Joe explains, "The first one is when you decide to watch out for other people's safety, your own safety awareness increases. Because you make it a practice to watch out for others' safety, you are, in fact, making it a practice to watch out for hazards and risky behaviors in general. In doing so, you will see hazards and potential situations everyday that could cause you or the ones you love to suffer an injury. You quickly improve your awareness and you are actually safer than before.

"I find it ironic," Joe continues, "That the motivation for watching out for others could actually be self-serving in its purpose. Either way, it doesn't matter; you are making yourself more aware and that benefits everyone."

Joe becomes silent and again transports Jeff to someplace new. They are watching a birthday party for an eleven-year-old boy. The boy asks his dad if he can use some fireworks for his birthday party. His dad responds it would be fine providing his son and his friends get them out and set them up. Then he would come out and supervise the fun.

About an hour later, his mom and dad are summoned to the backyard — all is ready. As the dad walks out the door, he looks up and smiles. Watching, Jeff realizes the smile is due to the fact his son and his seven friends are all wearing safety glasses.

Jeff asks Joe if the boy had been taught to always wear

safety glasses when using fireworks. Joe responds, "In a way he had, but not the way you would think. You see, over the years, the boy always saw his dad and any of his dad's friends wear safety glasses when helping with the Fourth of July fireworks. His dad didn't even learn it from a fireworks safety class; he had learned the principle and importance of eye protection on the job. One day, when he was lighting fireworks, he noticed a label on the side read, 'Caution: Shoots sparks five to six feet'. The boy's dad realized how hazardous this was because his eyes were between twelve and eighteen inches away while lighting the fireworks; well within the range of the sparks."

"His dad thought that if something went wrong he needed eye protection and went out and bought what he needed to be safe. So from that time on he always lit fireworks with safety glasses and that is what his son always saw. So wearing safety glasses in this situation became the natural thing to do. Once again, the father's focus on watching out for the safety of others increased his own awareness and helped him and his family be safe."

Joe continues, "Pretty impressive how watching out for other people increases your own awareness and protects you and the people you love."

"Sure," Jeff replies, "That alone would be a good enough reason to watch out for other people's safety."

"True," Joe responds, "But there are more reasons. Another reason to watch out for other people's safety is people can be distracted. There is so much going on in people's lives; it is amazing they can stay focused on any one thing. Obviously, if you were doing a hazardous task, total focus would be a necessity. But it is also important to be aware that the people you come in contact with, on and off the job, may be very distracted mentally and you would not know this until something goes wrong."

Once again, Jeff finds himself watching a scene in front of him. He sees a scoutmaster on the steps of the Empire State Building with a troop of Boy Scouts touring New York City on their way to the 1964 National Scout Jamboree at Valley Forge. They have traveled over three thousand miles to attend this scouting event and tour the country's historic sights. Over fifty thousand Boy Scouts had descended upon the East Coast.

A scout approaches his scoutmaster and informs him he came to the Jamboree with two hundred dollars and he has only spent thirty dollars, and the rest was missing. He suspects his tent mate had stolen it from his pack earlier that morning. The scoutmaster promises he would check into it.

During the day, the scoutmaster and his assistants do some checking. They discover the tent mate came with only five dollars and in the past two days had purchased merchandise which added up to over one hundred fifty dollars.

The scoutmaster and his assistant sit down with the boy who confesses he had taken the money and another scout's camera. He returns the camera and surrenders all the ill-gotten merchandise. Now, the scoutmaster has the unenviable task of calling the scout's mother to let her know what had happened. He turns the troop over to his assistants and then goes to a private place to call the scout's mom.

One of the ways you know you are dreaming is things occur that couldn't happen in real life. Jeff realizes he could see and hear both sides of the phone conversation. He watches as the scoutmaster places the call and at the same time he sees the scout's mom answering her phone at work, over three thousand miles away. She immediately shows concern on her face and in the tone of her voice as she wonders why her son's leader would be calling.

"Is he ok? Did he get hurt?" are thoughts that immediately come to her mind. The scoutmaster tells her what had happened and fills her in on the details. Her concern deepens. "What is going to happen? Would he be sent home?" are further thoughts coming to mind.

Mom listens as the scoutmaster explains the plan is for the scout to pay back the money and return the camera and then stay with the group while appropriate consequences are figured out. She looks around to see if anyone can hear her conversation, as she certainly doesn't want anyone to know about this incident.

She hangs up the phone and seems very stressed about what had happened so far away. Disappointment, embarrassment and concern are among the many emotions she is experiencing at this moment. She quickly changes her lunch plans to deliver a check to the Scout Office to pay back the scout who had his money taken. She tells a fellow worker she had to run a few errands and would have lunch off-site today.

Clearly, her fellow workers have no idea she is now in a distracted state of mind. It is unlikely she will be able to stay focused as she goes about her job that afternoon. She could easily not notice a hazard or forget to perform a safety procedure that is normally a part of her daily routine. Her normal routine for the day has changed dramatically.

Jeff thinks it is significant no one who works with her could be aware of her distracted state. They might see her near a hazard and logically think she had seen it. Because she was distracted, the hazard could be invisible to her and she could get hurt.

It is a certainty she will not tell anyone her son had stolen from another scout. Jeff wonders how many other people at her workplace had similar distractions, which are not public knowledge. Those are the kinds of distractions people tend to keep to themselves. Jeff continues to learn why it's important to watch out for everyone because it's impossible to know a person's mental state at any moment.

The scene before him fades and Joe returns. "I have never considered how distracted other people might be," Jeff comments.

Joe responds if more people realized this fact they would make it a point to watch out for each other and would feel much better about speaking up.

Jeff is getting excited about sharing this with other people he knows, "Are there any other reasons I can share, which would help them understand why they should watch out for each other's safety?"

"Sure, have you ever heard of a cognitive failure?" Joe asks.

"No," Jeff responds. Now, Jeff knows they were about to be transported to a new scene.

Jeff finds himself watching the intersection of a freeway off-ramp, a frontage road, and an intersecting street. He watches as a rather large truck pulls off the freeway onto the frontage road. The truck rolls to a stop at the stop sign, right in front of the cross street. The cross street is a country road with a small dashed line down the middle and a speed limit of fifty-five miles per hour.

As the truck rolls to a stop, Jeff sees a passenger vehicle approaching at about 35 miles per hour on the crossroad. Once again, he can hear people's thoughts as well as see what is happening. The driver of the passenger vehicle notices the truck and begins driving defensively. The driver of the passenger vehicle is pleased the truck driver had seen the stop sign and stopped.

Next, he notices the truck driver turning his head and looking right at him. In fact, in a defensive driving course he had taken it was noted you should always look to see if the other driver's eyes are looking right at you. It's claimed if another driver looks right into your eyes, you know they see you and you are okay. He then notices the truck driver look to his left. It is clear the situation he is approaching is safe. At least, that's what it looks like at this point.

Suddenly and without warning, the truck races forward right into the path of the passenger vehicle. The passenger vehicle slams into the truck and because the truck is going so fast, it drags the car 150 feet. The driver of the truck is totally surprised. He had looked and thought no one was there.

The driver of the car slammed up against the safety belt of his car and is safely restrained. The safety belt had done its job and he is fine. As everything comes to a halt, the driver slides out the passenger side door because the driver's side is destroyed and the car is totaled.

Jeff wonders why the truck driver had looked right at the driver of the car and still pulled forward. Joe, knowing Jeff's every thought and question speaks up, "The truck driver had a 'cognitive failure'. For one brief moment, the truck driver's brain failed him. The image of the passenger car went to the truck driver's eye and to his optic nerve. But when it went to the brain, there was a short failure and it never recorded."

"Wow," Jeff exclaims, "I would have sworn the truck driver had seen the car."

Joe enlightens him once again by explaining the cognitive failure could happen to anyone, anytime, and if the circumstances are just right, or wrong you might say, an injury could occur. Jeff wonders how someone could possibly defend against this kind of failure.

Having heard his thought, Joe answers, "The best way is to have the people around you watching out for you. That way, if you are near a hazard they can let you know. When no one else is around, double-checking would also help. If the truck driver had looked to the right one more time he might have seen the car."

Jeff comments to Joe, "I remember a time when I had a cognitive failure. I was looking all around my house trying to find my keys. I thought I had looked everywhere, so after several minutes of unsuccessful searching, I called out to my wife and asked her if she knew where my keys were. She walked into the kitchen and pointed to them right in front of me on the table in plain sight. I know I had looked there more than once, but I just didn't see them."

Joe replies, "That's a great example. Just imagine if the keys had been something hazardous you didn't see."

Jeff responds, "That's amazing, people could be distracted, or they could have a cognitive failure and if I point out the hazard to them they could avoid an injury. That seems to be a no-brainer. I'm going to point things out to people all the time now and I want to let other people know about all these reasons. Are there any other reasons for me to consider?"

"Sure," Joe answers, "One of them you already experienced in your first dream about the alternate ending to the cow incident. A great reason to watch out for other people's safety is so you know you will never feel the guilt and pain of knowing you could have prevented someone from being injured or killed."

Jeff reacts, "Imagine how the seven people who had walked

by Paul would have felt had he been hurt or killed? Every day when they entered their building they would be reminded of the incident as they walked past that point. That's a pain everyone wants to avoid. Are there any other reasons?"

Joe replies, "There are many reasons and it's exciting to me you've already decided it is worth watching out for others' safety at least two reasons ago." Joe follows up with, "Another reason to watch out for others' safety is that it is the right thing to do." There are times in life we just need to do what is right and safety is one of them.

"One other element you need to consider before you go out there helping people watch out for other people's safety is that many people feel uncomfortable pointing out something wrong to someone else. If they knew how to do this in a way that would be accepted and not insult the other person, it is more likely they would follow through."

"So, how can I make it easier for people to speak up?" Jeff asked. With that, the wheels of the airplane touched down and Jeff is jarred awake. He wonders what the answer to his last question is and how soon Joe would share it with him.

The first question which the priest and the Levite asked was: "If I stop to help this man, what will happen to me?" But... the Good Samaritan reversed the question: "If I do not stop to help this man, what will happen to him?"

                                        Martin Luther King, Jr.

Chapter Three

Asking for Help

Jeff had a great rest of the day. He never felt so rested as he did after his last flight. All he learned not only helped him, but he slept very deeply and was full of energy when he woke up. He visited with all the people he had planned to that day and was ready for a good night's sleep when he arrived at his hotel. He wonders if Joe will return in his dreams that night. He hopes so as he is looking forward to learning more and more.

As he falls off to sleep, Joe, the voice, returns. Jeff thanks Joe for coming back and once again asks how he could make himself and other people more comfortable watching out for other people's safety.

Tonight's lesson begins as Joe says, "One of the best ways to begin getting people to watch out for others' safety is to ask them to watch out for you. This is powerful for several reasons."

"First, you are taking personal responsibility for your own safety by making sure the people around you know you always want their input and the benefit of what they notice. Second, by asking them to watch out for you, they get practice watching out for someone they know wants their help."

Joe points out, "It's best to ask people to watch out for you one to one. Where you are going next will make that very clear."

Jeff is then looking in on a big manufacturing plant's safety meeting. The plant manager, who Jeff knows is truly committed to safety, is doing an exercise to really facilitate his employees watching out for each other. He walks up to the microphone and says, "Each and everyone of us should be our brothers' keepers and always watch out for each other. You need to let everyone know you want them to watch out for you."

Jeff is excited the plant manager seemingly has the right idea. The plant manager continues, "I want everyone here who wants the people they work with to watch out for their safety to please stand up."

Because Jeff can hear people's thoughts, it is as if the room became a din of conversation. It isn't conversation though; it is people reacting to the plant manager's request. Jeff hears, "I hate standing up, is he kidding?"

"I don't think everyone standing wants people to watch out for them, they just want the boss to see they were willing to do what he asks. In fact, the first guy to stand up is such a kiss up; I know he is just showing off."

Another person thinks, "I'm standing and I don't really know if I agree. I wonder how many other people are doing the same thing."

Jeff begins to realize everything is going wrong. The people are doing something as a group only because of the pressure of the moment. It looks like success, yet it isn't.

The boss is thrilled, seeing that after a few appeals he has everyone standing. Jeff turns to Joe and says, "That's amazing, you are really right. It seems great at first, yet when you can hear what people are really thinking it is a whole different story." Joe nods in agreement.

Joe brings Jeff to a small break room and there are two workers having lunch. One of them looks at the other and says, "Remember what that magician safety speaker said the other day about watching out for each other?"

His friend replies, "Yes."

"Well," he continues. "I would really appreciate it if you would watch out for my safety. I know my job and now I know anyone can have a moment of distraction or a cognitive failure. So, would you watch out for me?"

"Sure," his friend replies and, "Would you also watch out for me?"

"You bet," is the sincere reply.

Jeff notes the thoughts of the two people sitting at the lunch table are congruent with the words they spoke. He watches them shake hands as they go back to work.

Joe notes, "As with all person-to-person communication, it's possible to get feedback and assess the other person's reaction. It also gives each of them the opportunity to ask the other person to return the favor."

Jeff is then watching another interaction. One guy among a group of workers walks up to one of his co-workers and says, "George, you know how they always talk about safety around here. Well, I want to let you know I would really appreciate it if you would watch out for my safety. I never know when I might be distracted or fail to notice a hazard and I would be grateful if you see me near any hazard to point it out to me even if you think I am aware of it."

"I heard this great safety speaker who does magic tricks talk about how a competent person can be looking right at something and not see it. Something he called a cognitive failure. Anyway, please watch out for me and if you want I will do the same for you."

George responds, "No problem, Jerry, I'd be glad to and I'd appreciate it if you did the same for me."

Joe comments, "In addition to asking people to watch out for you, it is equally important to react appropriately when they do. Watch this..."

Jeff and Joe are floating above a car traveling down the freeway.

Joe explains, "You are going to see someone change from not wanting someone to watch out for him to actually asking for that help."

Jeff and Joe could see and hear right inside the car even over the noise of the freeway traffic. The car is going about 65 miles per hour with a gentleman and his wife in the car. Suddenly, the wife in the passenger seat exclaims, "Brake lights ahead."

The driver barks back at her, "I know how to drive." He isn't too interested in her input and this rude response is not good for their relationship. Thus, this is not a good response from either a safety or relationship perspective.

Joe clicks his fingers and says, "Now, watch what happens after the same driver hears a talk called, 'Would You Watch Out For My Safety©?"

Once again, Jeff sees the couple in the car traveling down a freeway. The wife sees brake lights ahead and calls out, "Brake lights!"

This time the driver responds with, "Thanks for watching out for us, I did see them but keep telling me." This was a much better response. He is still able to sooth his ego, inform her he saw them and let her know he appreciated her attention.

It's a good thing he did because a few miles ahead an impaired driver is in the lane next to them. The driver is focused on how to avoid that car's erratic movements and not collide with the cars around them. His attention is diverted from the lane in front of him for a very good reason. As he deals with this problem he glances back into his lane every couple of seconds, but that isn't the location of his primary focus.

During a moment when he is watching the unpredictable vehicle in the other lane, his wife calls out again, "Brake lights." He looks and quickly applies the brakes, keeping him and his wife safe. Her attention and his encouraging her to give him input gave him a second or two, which on a freeway is quite a long distance of travel and a large margin of safety. He thanks her again and really brought the message home when he later brings her flowers, thanking her for caring about their safety.

Joe adds, "Obviously, the driver is a lot safer and he is going to have a better relationship with his wife."

As the morning light shines through the window, Jeff wakes up and realizes he had another great night of sleep and some great lessons. He now knows why everyone should watch out for each other's safety and why we should ask others to watch out for our safety. He wonders what is next when he remembers Joe promises he would show him how to be comfortable pointing out hazards and unsafe behaviors to people.

If you think you are too small to be effective, you have never been in bed with a mosquito.

Betty Reese

Chapter Four

Making It Comfortable

Another terrific day had gone smoothly and Jeff is off to the airport for the flight home. Before he knows it, Jeff is on the plane nodding off to sleep right before take off. Sure enough, as soon as he dozes off, Joe's voice returns in his dreams again. Excited, Jeff exclaims, "Hi Joe, great to hear from you again!"

Joe responds, "It's my pleasure, especially as quickly as you are learning about helping others stay safe on and off the job."

"So, what's next?" Jeff asks.

Joe replies, "Well, you now know why you should want to watch out for other people's safety and ask those around you to watch out for your safety. Now, it's time to learn how to point out safety to others and feel good about it."

The next thing Jeff knows, he is out in the country looking at a two-lane road with a yellow line down the middle. He can see a man, Tom, at the end of a long driveway amongst little country properties. He is getting his mail. Jeff notices, as does the person at the mailbox, two ladies, Kathy and Doris, walking along the country road.

Tom notices a hazardous behavior immediately. Kathy and Doris are walking on both sides of the road. This means if a driver had trouble with their vehicle it didn't matter which way they swerved, one of the ladies was going to die. Jeff hears the thoughts of the man at the mailbox, "Should I say something to these ladies? I see them walking every day, which is great for their health, yet they are doing something that could get them hurt or killed." Jeff cheers for Tom to stay and say something to them. Tom thinks further, "What will they think if I say something?" He decides to stay and point it out to Kathy and Doris.

As they arrive at the mailbox, Tom says hello and they respond in kind. He then says, "I notice the two of you walking every day and I really admire that. It's great for your health but I notice you do something that's very unsafe. You're walking on either side of the street and if I have trouble with my car, I have to decide which one of you to kill."

He then says, "What you might want to do is both walk on the side of the road facing the oncoming traffic since there's no sidewalk here. When you walk facing the traffic, if somebody's in trouble you could see a car's not in control so you could jump out of its way and give yourself a fighting chance. At the very least, the driver could swerve the other way and not hit either one of you."

Joe intercedes with a comment, "Jeff, be sure to notice how much the ladies praise the man for helping them be safe. You may be surprised what happens next."

Doris adds, "Thanks for taking the time to say something. We saw you standing there and were wondering what you were waiting for. Not many people would care enough to do anything. That's really neat; thank you for doing that. Thank you for actively caring."

Tom responds, "You're welcome; you would do the same for me," and climbs back in his van and drives down the road. Everything seems great. Great until Jeff hears the next thought going through Tom's mind. He thinks, "What if the two ladies think I am a jerk?"

What a surprise! Jeff ponders where that thought came from. After all, just moments ago, they praised Tom for what he did and how much he cared for their safety.

Joe chimes in with the answer, "Remember the questions Tom asked himself when the ladies were about one hundred yards away? He asked himself if he should say something and he obviously answered that question with a yes. The next question he asked himself is where the doubt came from because he asked, 'What will they think?'"

Jeff listens intently as Joe continues, "You see, he asked the wrong question. The human brain is an amazing creation. It can operate faster than any computer and it can handle many tasks and thought processes at the same time. In this case, the man at the mailbox asked the question and while he was waiting and talking to the ladies, his brain was formulating all the possible answers to the question, what will they think?"

"As soon as he was done talking to them and driving away, his brain began to give him the data it had been working on. It just so happens the first one to pop up was, they might think he was a jerk."

"So, what is the answer to this one, Joe?"

"Well, let's go somewhere else and find out," Joe responds.

Jeff finds himself in the audience of the magician safety speaker, this time in Rock Springs, Wyoming. The safety speaker has a volunteer on stage and he notices the volunteer's shoelace is untied. It is a college lecture hall and in order for the volunteer to get back to his seat he must walk back up some stairs.

The safety speaker thinks to himself, "What do I do? If I let him go back to his seat without saying something, he could trip and get hurt." The speaker wonders how to let him know about the hazard in a comfortable manner. Then it comes to him and he asks the volunteer, "Would you like me to watch out for your safety?"

The volunteer reacts, "What?"

The safety speaker repeats, "Would you like me to watch out for your safety?"

The volunteer says, "Sure!"

The safety speaker tells him about his shoelace and suggests he sit down in the front row and retie it before returning to his seat. That's exactly what he does.

Jeff listens to the safety speaker's thoughts and finds it interesting the speaker had no doubtful thoughts about what he said to the volunteer.

Joe responds to Jeff's thought with, "You see this time the person asked a better question. He asked the volunteer himself if he wanted him to watch out for his safety. Tom, asked a hypothetical question in his own mind instead of asking the ladies themselves. The safety speaker knew the volunteer wanted the input because he had just given his permission to give the safety advice."

Jeff wonders what the safety speaker would have done had the volunteer said no to the question.

Joe says, "I know what he would have done, in fact, I know this speaker very well. You see, years ago, I gave him his first big break in the safety business. He's quite a character. He would have stepped on the guy's shoelace and tripped him — he can always use a new story." "Actually, that's an exaggeration. I know him well enough to know he would have said something anyway. Besides, the safety speaker knows what I know. Almost always the person is going to say 'yes' because at the very least they are curious about what you have in mind."

Joe proudly adds, "That safety speaker dedicated his first book, *Mastering Safety Communication* to me. You should go online and get a copy." [1]

Jeff comments to Joe, "Don't some people hesitate to point out a hazard to someone who is experienced and is a skilled craftsperson? I mean, who am I to say something to someone who has more experience than I?"

Joe responds, "While that may be the case for some people, you need to remember about the possibility of that experienced person having a cognitive failure. Remember, a cognitive failure has no respect for experience, skill, knowledge or intelligence; everyone is vulnerable."

"Once I was watching a shop steward, Pat, sharing with members of the International Brotherhood of Electrical Workers what he had learned about cognitive failures. Clearly, Pat was talking to people who knew their job. They were skilled craftspeople who knew what they were doing. However, Pat understood that even his best person could experience a cognitive failure and when this happens, someone watching out for his or her safety could make all the difference in the world."

Joe continues, "In fact, the more experienced a person is, the more likely they would have lived through one of these cognitive failures during their career and realize how important it is for us to watch out for each other."

---

[1] Mastering Safety Communication available at: www.drebinger.com

Jeff points out, "I've noticed that out on the bike trail. I ride a bike about six miles a day for fitness and everywhere I go, all the experienced riders are wearing safety helmets and gloves. It is the amateurs who have their kids in helmets because it's the law and then ride without one themselves. The experienced riders, even though they have more skill than the amateurs, know the consequences of a fall and are going to do what it takes to protect themselves."

Joe asks Jeff, "Would you like to know a great way to share a safety concern with an experienced worker?"

"Sure," Jeff replies.

Joe responds, "When you see someone near a hazard all you need do is say, 'As you know, there is a hazard there."

"That would have worked well for the workers in the substation where Bob was injured. They could have seen him on that ladder near the power source and said, 'Hey Bob, as you know there is a power supply right next to your shoulder.' Bob wouldn't have to admit he didn't know it was there. He could have responded by saying, 'Thanks, I know it's there, and keep watching out for me."

Joe continues, "That would have been great for the people who saw the young painter's apprentice scraping the grating as well. They could have easily said, 'As you know, there is a power supply under that grate."

Jeff responds, "I can really see how well such a simple phrase makes it easier to share safety with someone."

Joe replies, "It is amazing that oftentimes the best solution is easier than people think. I believe sometimes people feel compelled to complicate something so simple. Maybe it's a function of how complex our world seems to have become, influencing people to look for intricate solutions."

"My friend, the safety speaker who uses magic in his presentations, would tell you that many of the best magic tricks are also the simplest. He would also tell you that one of the reasons most people can never figure out how his magic tricks are done is that they are looking for far too complicated a solution. So, remember to keep it simple and easy when you are watching out for other people's safety."

Jeff wonders, "What about locations that have work rules or policies that define in detail who has the right to supervise or give job instructions or directions to someone?"

Joe replies, "That's a great question, Jeff. Remember to keep it simple. When you are watching out for someone else's safety you aren't telling them how to do their job or what job they are supposed to do. That is clearly the responsibility of their supervisor. You are simply letting them know of a hazard or behavior you have noticed, which could lead to them being injured."

Jeff asks Joe, "What if you don't have time to ask someone or to say, 'As you know' before offering advice?"

Joe replies, "Good point. Sometimes in an emergency or severe situation, you need to point something out immediately or yell a warning. When this happens, the person watching out for someone else's safety doesn't worry about the response they will get. The person who is being helped might react negatively at first and then later be grateful."

"What if they respond negatively?" Jeff asks. "If you use these communication techniques are people always going to respond in a favorable way?"

Joe answers, "Not always."

"Then what do you do if someone responds negatively?" Jeff inquires. "What if somebody says, 'Leave me alone,' or 'Hey, would you get out of here. I've got to get this job finished,' or even 'I saw that. What do you think I am, stupid?' What if they acted this way? What should someone do in that case?"

Joe replies, "First, it's great you asked this question now. I have found that when people think of what to do ahead of time they communicate more effectively. There are several ways to handle this. I'll show you a strategy I've seen people use very well.

Now, Jeff is in a manufacturing facility. One worker is doing his job when a fellow worker walks in and notices a hazard that might be a problem. He walks over and says, "Hey Gary, did you see that...?"

Gary barks back, "Of course I did, I've been doing this job for eighteen years and I know what to do."

The helpful worker responds, "Sorry, I just want to make sure you make it home safely." As he walks away, Joe and Jeff could hear his thoughts. It was great he didn't feel put off. In fact, he quickly was able to put things in the right perspective. The thoughts they heard were, "Wow, I guess Gary is having a tough day. I understand he knows his job and if he were not so stressed out he wouldn't have reacted that way."

He went on to think of other times when Gary had been upset and someone he cared about walked into the room and he shouted at them. He knew it wasn't about him; it was more about Gary. Since it wasn't really about him it was easy to brush it off. He also thought that even though Gary said he saw the hazard, it is possible he might not have and was just being defensive. Either way, Gary wasn't going to get hurt because the helpful worker cared enough to say something.

Suddenly, they aren't in the factory any more. They are on a job site where a similar incident was about to take place. As Jeff and Joe arrive, they see a worker respond unkindly to a safety concern expressed by another person. The person who had just pointed out the risky behavior steps back, smiles and says, "Hey, that's ok. Can you do me a favor and wait for me to get my video camera because when things go wrong it will make a great video for YouTube!"

His friend looks up and laughs. It was the perfect response and he got the message. Sometimes humor is a great way to break the tension with the right person.

Joe comments, "By the way, a negative reaction doesn't happen all that often. It really doesn't. Most of the time, people appreciate it. Once again, if you ask them, 'Would you like me to watch out for your safety?' you will likely get a positive response."

Joe continues, "Remember the fifth reason people should watch out for someone else's safety?

Jeff replies, "Sure, it's the right thing to do."

Joe responds, "That's right and it can also be helpful in this situation. Sometimes in life, because you are doing the right thing you will encounter someone who doesn't value safety the way you do or doesn't understand that injuries are preventable. Those people may respond in a negative way. Let me take you to a place where a person did just the right thing with someone who had some unresourceful beliefs about safety."

Now Jeff finds himself standing at a gas station. It is a hot July day and at one of the pumps a person is pumping gas and smoking a cigarette. Another car pulls up and a man gets out to get his gas. He sees the person smoking and immediately thinks this is incredibly unsafe. Most smokers know this is an unsafe behavior and care enough about themselves and others to never smoke near a gas pump. Apparently, this smoker wasn't as considerate as most.

Jeff, being able to hear thoughts, also discovers the second man, Andy, is the plant manager at a nearby oil refinery. Andy walks over to the island with the person pumping gas and starts up a conversation. He calmly says, "You know it's very dangerous to be smoking while you are pumping gas."

The person replies by giving him some suggestions as to where he might want to go on his next vacation. Slightly startled by the language used, he decides to give the person a more detailed reason why this was a particularly bad choice of behavior in this situation.

"Maybe you didn't realize it but the car next to yours has two children inside strapped into car seats. If your car broke into flames just the radiant heat from that explosion would cause massive burns to their tender young skin. Also, if the explosion and fire hit their vehicle we might not be able to get them out in time to save their lives. I really would appreciate it if you would please put the cigarette out."

The person pumping gas responded negatively again with another display of foul language.

Jeff could hear Andy thinking, "Ok, he isn't going to put the cigarette out. What can I do to keep him and everyone around here safe?" He knew just what to do. Jeff watches as the refinery manager walks over to the wall of the gas station building and hits the emergency shut-off valve. All the gas pumps come to a halt and everyone looks over at him.

Andy points at the person with the cigarette and says he wants to make sure the smoker doesn't get anyone hurt. At that point, everyone looks at the person with the cigarette. The station operator comes out to find out what is going on and makes sure the cigarette is out before turning on the pumps again.

Andy finishes up, gets in his car and drives off. Even though his comments and subsequent action weren't received with open arms and praise, he knew it was the right thing to do. Sometimes, it takes courage to do the right thing.

Jeff realizes one thing for sure; that refinery manager will never have the nightmare of seeing someone hurt he could have protected. If the person who was being careless was going to cause an injury, it wasn't going to happen on his watch.

Joe comments to Jeff, "Sometimes the mere satisfaction of knowing you have done the right thing is enough to soothe the abrasive response some people might give. No negative response will ever carry the same pain as knowing you let someone be injured."

Let each of you look not only to his own interests, but also to the interests of others.

Philippians 2:4

Chapter Five

Responding to Help Others

Joe shares a new idea with Jeff, "Up until now, we have been focused on how to share safety with someone else and yet all communication has two sides. One of the most important things you can do to help yourself and others be safe is to respond in the best way possible."

"Jeff, let me show you a situation where this happened. Interestingly enough, it was at a safety meeting for a company that cared about safety. They have special safety meetings for their employees where they bring in a professional safety speaker to remind them of how important it is to watch out for each other's safety."

Transported to a new location, in the audience of this safety meeting, Jeff watches as the safety speaker asks someone in the audience for a dollar bill. [2] Several people offer and the safety speaker takes the first one available. He smiles and says, "Thank You," as he put the dollar bill into his pocket.

With that little joke, he takes the dollar back out and brings a volunteer on the stage, hands them the dollar bill and asks them to read the serial number. The safety speaker writes the number down on a large Post It® Note flip chart. He steps out of the way and asks the volunteer to read the number once again so everyone can verify he had written it down exactly as read. He takes the large paper and hands it to the person who gave him the dollar bill and says, "Here is

---

[2] To see a video of this magic trick go on the internet to: www.drebinger.com

your receipt." The audience laughs as the speaker returns to the stage.

He then instructs the volunteer to tear the dollar bill in half. The volunteer looks at him as if he thinks the safety speaker is kidding. "No, I'm serious. Tear up the dollar." Reluctantly, the volunteer tears up the dollar bill. The safety speaker then announces it is a federal offense to tear up United States currency. Once again, the audience chuckles. He then takes the bill, saying he wouldn't ask the volunteer to do anything he wouldn't do himself and he tears the dollar again into four pieces.

The speaker quickly comments to the person who gave him the dollar, "Now you have four quarters, just don't try and use them in a vending machine." He holds the pieces in plain sight and with a wave of his hand they vanish. He exclaims, "Now you have a problem. That guy in the audience is going to want his dollar back and I have just the solution."

"As you may have noticed, this lemon has been sitting on the stage since the beginning of my presentation. Watch!" The safety speaker picks up the lemon and a knife and he slices the lemon in half. Leaving it intact, he hands it to the volunteer on stage and instructs them to twist it apart. They do so and to everyone's amazement there is what appears to be a dollar bill rolled up in the center of the lemon. The volunteer unrolls it and reads off the serial number that matches the number on the receipt for the original bill that had been destroyed. The audience breaks into applause.

Jeff watches after the presentation and notices someone approach the safety speaker. The person introduces himself as Jerry and asks the speaker if he would like him to watch out for his safety. As the speaker responds yes, he looks around the stage and on his prop table to see if he could notice what the person has observed.

Jerry then says, "I noticed you cut the lemon during that last magic trick and I would hate to see you get cut doing it."

The safety speaker responds, "Yeah, that would be very embarrassing to get cut during a safety presentation."

Jerry then offers, "We have some special leather gloves that are Kevlar-lined. Would you like me to get you a pair?"

"Sure!" is the safety speaker's response. Jerry brings a pair of gloves back and gives them to the speaker who is grateful and says, "Thanks, I will be sure to use them in all my future presentations. Also, thank you for watching out for my safety!"

A couple weeks later, the safety speaker is doing the "dollar-bill-in-the-lemon trick" again and afterwards another gentleman comes up to him, introduces himself as Jack, and says, "Would you like me to watch out for your safety?"

The speaker replies, "You bet."

Jack then says, "I noticed when you are cutting the lemon you wear leather gloves and those are good. We have gloves that are Kevlar and are more cut-resistant than leather. You could cut through the leather with a sharp knife."

Joe chimes in, "Jeff, do you realize what is happening? Initially what Jack said seems to only affect the speaker's safety. However, how the safety speaker responds to Jack will shape both Jack's actions with other people in the future and the future safety of those individuals. The safety speaker's response will definitely influence whether Jack will choose to help other people in the future."

Joe continues, "Once somebody points out a hazard to you, you're now aware of the hazard. You have benefitted from the advice and I'm sure you would want others to continue benefitting from Jack's observations. It's the very next person he comes in contact with that the speaker's response is going to affect.

Now, remember Jack was telling the safety speaker about the Kevlar cut-resistant gloves. Remember, also, the leather gloves the safety speaker had were Kevlar-lined. No one knew that except the safety speaker himself. The speaker could have said to him, "Oh, hey, don't sweat it, these have a Kevlar lining." Yet he chose not to. I wonder why."

Jeff begins to understand this whole concept more and more. He says, "If the safety speaker had done that, it is possible Jack would have felt like he was being put down. Jack may have felt foolish that he didn't realize the safety speaker would have had the best gloves. Jack could have walked away thinking he shouldn't have said anything. It would have made him feel uncomfortable about watching out for other people's safety in the future. Because he was helping the safety speaker, it was important for the speaker to encourage the correct behavior."

Jeff continues, "We know people will do things with which they are comfortable and we always want them to feel comfortable watching out for someone else's safety. Imagine if the next person Jack sees near a hazard is doing something much more hazardous than cutting a lemon. He thinks, 'Oh, should I say something?' How horrible would it be if he'd gotten ridiculed the last time he decided to watch out for someone's safety and, as a result, he keeps his mouth shut and the next person gets hurt?"

Joe says, "You are really getting good at this and the best part is you understand the principles behind why it works."

Jeff replies, "So, what else do you want to teach me?

Joe responds, "Actually nothing. You now have all you need to go out there and help other people work safely. In fact, you have more than that, you have the tools to help them watch out for others' safety."

Jeff says, "Ok, but are you sure I don't need more? It seems like it should take a long time to be able to do this."

Joe smiles and said, "Remember what I told you about how people want to make things more complicated? Well, that is an easy trap in which to fall. Sure, you could get lots of safety training yet even an untrained person can spot hazards out there in the world. That magician safety speaker once told me a saying his dad would often say, 'The better is the enemy of the good.' What you have now, Jeff is good. The most important thing now is to put it to work and to teach it to others."

"Will I be seeing you again?" Jeff asks.

"Sure, I will probably be cheering you on now and then. I will drop by to remind you of the impact you are having. Maybe in the future, I can take you around and show you how to help people avoid shortcuts. Have fun Jeff and may God bless you and every person who watches out for the safety of God's children.

With that, the wheels of the plane hit the ground and Jeff awakens to find himself back home in Sacramento.

"If you think education is expensive, try ignorance."

- Derek Bok

Chapter Six

Reasons We Should Watch Out for Other People's Safety

I hope you enjoyed the story told in the first five chapters of this book. If you skipped the story to join me at this point of the book, welcome, you haven't missed a thing. From this point on, I discuss the techniques of watching out for other people's safety like I do when I am giving one of my presentations on the subject. For those of you who read the first five chapters, you will find this a rewording of the concepts you have already learned. The stories I refer to are basically the same but not in novel format. So, however you arrived at this page, let's get going.

You and I do everything we do for a reason and it is important to understand the "why" of what motivates everyone. One of most important elements left out of motivating people to watch out for others' safety is to help them find their answer to the question, "Why should I watch out for everyone's safety?"

No matter what you do, you have a reason to work safely and watch out for the safety of others. At one of my presentations, a corporate leader made a comment I thought was outstanding. He said, "You know, one of the advantages we have here is we don't have a 1,500 pound steam pipeline going through our building. And do you know one of the disadvantages we have here? We don't have a 1,500 pound steam pipeline going through our building. If we did, we would be more aware of the importance of safety. There would be a perceived risk which would cause us to be more mindful of safety."

What jobs do you think would put you at the highest risk to be injured? Perhaps another way of looking at this is what job would you not want your children to take?

Some of the answers people give are: working on an oil rig, an Alaskan crab fisherman, ironworker, or coal miner. Recently, I was in a coal mine, 1,600 feet underground, learning about the work my audience was doing every day. As a point of reference, we were down there during the time when the Chilean miners were trapped underground. That type of event increases the perceived danger. Some other jobs perceived to be risky are taxicab driver and convenience store clerk. I can really relate to that. When my daughter went out looking for a job, I told her, "You can take any job you want as long as when you're walking out, there's not one of those stickers on the wall that has a height chart and a video camera taking a picture of the person who just shot at you."

After all the ideas were pointed out, I shared the following information with them. The place in their company where the majority of the injuries occurred was in the office building in which they were working. The people to whom I was talking have more injuries than the people doing the hazardous tasks. For the workers in the hazardous areas, they have a pretty good reason to work safely, right? When they get up in the morning, they go to work at a job where if something went wrong it could kill them. They begin the day and ask themselves, "Should I work safely or die?" That's an easy decision because they don't get a second chance. But the people in the office get up and they think, "Hey, what's the worst thing that could happen to me here? A paper cut? Whoa." Then they walk down the stairs and don't use the handrail, slip and fall and get hurt severely. They begin to pick something up, they hurt their back and for the rest of their life, they are in pain all because they picked up something incorrectly in an office, where it was perceived to be safe.

The same is true for the people doing the hazardous work. They can go through the day totally focused on safety when they are doing the hazardous activities and then they let their guard down. Are you familiar with the Winter Olympics and the snowboarder, Shaun White? He's the guy with the long, red hair. He was on the *Tonight Show*, talking to Jay Leno, and he told a great safety story. He was talking about having focused on snowboarding and now he's getting back into skateboarding. He was in a series of skateboarding competitions and had to miss a couple of them due to an injury. Of course, everyone assumed he got hurt at the skateboard park honing his skills.

He related he was at a skateboard park in Venice Beach, California. He and the other skateboarders were doing crazy stuff. He had a great day and, no, he didn't get hurt then. It was at the end of the day, he said, "As I was leaving the skate park, walking back to my car, I tripped on a curb and twisted my ankle." Shaun was doing something that could potentially kill him if he does it wrong. In his sport, he flies upside down over cement. Even with a helmet on, if you hit right (or wrong) you could break your neck. Now, when he was done with that hazardous situation, he let his guard down resulting in an injury. How ironic was that?

That kind of stuff happens all the time. It tells us we need to watch out for our safety 100 percent of the time - the big stuff and the little stuff. In fact, for the little stuff, we probably need to raise our guard because our mind isn't as focused on the danger.

So, why would people want to watch out for each other's safety? Why would anybody be interested in watching out for somebody else? Why would that be important?

One of the benefits of watching out for other people's safety is that it helps protect you. I teach people during one of my talks, entitled "Ensure Your Safety," each one of us needs to watch out for our own safety. It's all about taking personal responsibility. I picked that up very early in my career in safety. I listened to a lot of safety professionals say that 90 to 95 percent of the time, when an injury occurred, the person who was injured could have either eliminated the injury, or lessened the effect. I wear a vehicle safety belt and that protects me. I do things safely, I benefit. I'm the one that ultimately suffers the consequence of any injury; therefore, I need to take personal responsibility for my own safety.

When somebody gets hurt, who really pays for the injury? Insurance companies and government agencies? No, the injured person is the one who pays. Businesses write checks but they don't get injured. They don't deal with the pain. In the case of property damage, it is also true. For example, when you get hit driving your car and it's 100 percent their fault. Who's going to pay for it? They are, but again, who goes through the hassle? You've got to get repair estimates and get it fixed. Even though it gets restored, you're the one who deals with the pain.

I teach people to take personal responsibility. When I started speaking about people's safety over 20 years ago, I started noticing hazards I never would have seen before. My guess is everyone is like that. You spot dangers of which you would never have been aware. You see hazards, and even when you're doing stuff for yourself at home, you think about safety. You're focused on safety, and you're more alert. You're thinking in those terms. So, therefore, you benefit when you watch out for other people. "Hey, I'm going to go to work today and I'm going to watch out for all the hazards of everybody I work with. I'm going to pay attention to them." When you look out for everyone else, you also notice the hazards that could injure you.

As an example, the stage is a part of my work area. One of the things I'm constantly aware of when I bring somebody up on the stage is their safety. I never let them get within one foot of the edge of the stage. Why? Because they're not used to it and they could easily miss the edge and fall off.

The more you watch out for other people, the safer you become and your family's safety improves. How cool is that? You really benefit by watching out for other people.

The second reason to watch out for other people's safety is they may be distracted. It seems there are more distractions today than ever before. Interesting thought. I can think of all sorts of distractions — both internal and external. Since you don't always know what's going on in a person's life, it's very likely you won't know when they are distracted.

For me, the day my mom passed away I am sure I was distracted. I received a call at four in the morning. The doctor said, "You need to come up to the hospital. She's not going to make it through the day."

I got in the car and drove to the hospital. My guess is at four in the morning, heading to the hospital, I might have been a little distracted while driving. I had a wonderful relationship with my parents, yet that morning, I am sure I wasn't a good example of a focused driver. It probably would have helped the other drivers if they knew that information, except you and they don't have the ability to read people's minds.

Another incident comes to mind when someone would have been distracted without anyone knowing. It was at the National Jamboree of the Boy Scouts. Having flown back east with scouts from Southern California to New York City, a scoutmaster is approached by a scout who explained he came with $200, had spent $50 and the rest was missing. He thought his tent mate had stolen it. Oh, boy, one of the fun jobs of being a scoutmaster. The scoutmaster and his assistant met with the scout in question and within minutes, the boy admitted he had taken the money and another scout's camera on the bus.

Now, it's the scoutmaster's unenviable job to call the scout's mom and let her know what has happened and the consequences of that action. The scoutmaster called her and said, "We've got a little problem here. Your son stole one hundred fifty dollars from another scout and also a camera." The scout leader told her the camera had been returned and the money would have to be replaced so it could be given back to the scout who had brought it. You can probably imagine how it would feel if your kids let you down — you would be disappointed and worried.

You can presume she was a little distracted that day and probably the next. She wouldn't be her best on the job. Keep this scary thought in mind; nobody where she works is going to know about it. She's not going to come to work that day and declare, "Hey, guess what my kid did?" She's not going to be telling everybody at the office that her kid stole one hundred fifty dollars. That's just not going to happen. You can bet she's thinking about her child on the other side of the country and what he had done.

She's got to be distracted. Yet the people around her don't know that. Perhaps they notice her near a hazard. They see her next to it and maybe she doesn't. Have you been distracted so much that you don't see something? We've all experienced that. That hazard could cause her to get hurt. Whether somebody says something at that moment can make a huge difference to her.

That's one of the reasons you need to watch out for each other. She's not likely to be looking out for herself at that moment. She's distracted. So, therefore, we need to watch out for each other. The people you work with could be distracted as much as she, or worse. And you'd never know. There are a lot of things happening out there you're not aware of. We need to watch out for each other because once in a while we have one of those days when we're not at our best. So, watching out for people at that time is critical.

A third reason to watch out for other people is just plain old brain failure. Not distraction, but your brain actually fails you. The behavioral psychologists will tell you there are certain times when a human brain will fall short and fail to notice something, called a cognitive failure. I'm sure you have experienced it.

I can tell you how it affected my life. I was driving down the road one time, going about fifty-five miles per hour. I live in Galt, California, about a half hour south of Sacramento. I was heading down a little country road with a yellow line down the middle of the road. As I approached Highway 99, I started slowing down because I was going to turn and get on the freeway. As I slowed down, I saw a truck pull off on the frontage road and come to a stop at the stop sign.

Then I saw him turn and look right at me. I thought, what a great deal. In defensive driving class, they always teach you to actually turn your head and look, don't just glance, don't just look in your rear-view mirror. This guy literally took his whole head, moved it and looked right at me. Then, he turned and looked the other way. I was thinking this is great. He stopped at the stop sign, looked my way and the other way. Life is good.

Suddenly, when I was just a few feet before the intersection, the truck pulled in front of me so fast when I hit him he dragged me 150 feet in his direction. I literally went back later and measured. His truck and my car were totaled. I had to slide out the passenger side of the car. The force with which I hit the safety belt was tremendous. I was shocked. If I hadn't been buckled up, I'd have blown through the windshield, scaring small animals and children. They would have been saying, "Whoa, what was that? An eclipse?" You may laugh, but I wouldn't be here today to make that joke if it weren't for what I did by clicking on my safety belt five minutes earlier as I got into the car.

The reason I tell this story is to let you know what happened to the other driver. There were two things that caused the collision. First, he had what we call a cognitive failure and second, he chose to rush. When the Highway Patrolman showed up, the truck driver said to him, "I looked and he wasn't there."

I replied, "You got it half right. You did look." He had looked right at me. I saw him. The image went from me to his eye, to the optic nerve and it didn't record. That was the cognitive failure.

The safety mistake he made was when he turned and looked the other way. He saw a car coming and he made the assessment, "If I hurry, I can beat that car across the intersection." That was the safety error. If you ever hear your brain say, "Hurry up!" Don't do it. That action destroyed his truck.

What were my choices in that situation? My choices were to swerve left, in which case I still would have hit the truck, because of its length. If I'd swerved to the right, I would have hit a utility pole. Neither was a good choice. The best decision I made that day was to click my safety belt around my shoulder and waist. That permitted me to walk away from that crash, allowing me to give my daughter a hug that afternoon.

Sometimes in life, it doesn't matter who's at fault. The other driver was 100 percent at fault. His insurance company didn't argue at all. Even though I was one hundred percent right, if I had been killed, what consolation would that have been to my wife and daughter standing next to my gravesite

saying, "God bless him, Dad was right. But he's dead."
There are certain times in life when you don't get points for
being right. Safety's one of them. You can be 100 percent
right and dead.

A cognitive failure can happen to anyone. We've all had a
cognitive failure. Have you ever looked for something
around the house? For example, you can't find your keys.
You look all over and you just can't find your keys. So,
finally, you give up. You elicit the help of somebody else in
your family, "Help, I can't find my keys."

Don't you hate it when they walk in the room, point at the
table right in front of you, in plain sight, and there are the
keys. We've all had that experience.

An audience member shared a great example. He and his
wife were at the park with their children one day and
suddenly he realized he didn't know the whereabouts of his
daughter. Excitedly, he called out to his wife, "Where is
Zoe? I can't find her." His wife laughed and informed him
that his daughter was sitting on his shoulders.

I'm sure there are people working with you who are very
competent and you're glad they're with you. Yet, if they
have a cognitive failure, they could be looking right at a
hazard and not see it. At that moment in their life, their
safety is dependent upon whether you say something.

You see, sometimes it makes a difference what you do for
your own safety, or what you do for someone else's safety.
What you do for someone else can make the difference
when their brain fails them.

The fourth reason to watch out for others' safety is of
benefit to you. This reason is to avoid the personal pain or
guilt of realizing you could have done something. I almost

had one of those. We were driving to the airport at 4:10 in the morning. My wife, Karen, was in the car with me. It was pitch black outside and I was zipping down the road. As we were driving along, I decided to change the radio station.

All of a sudden, I hear her yell, "Cow!" I look up and at first I don't see a cow. Finally, I see a little white stripe on the top of this very big animal and I swerved to miss it. Karen watched out for our safety and said something. It's a good thing because I was distracted at that moment. If she hadn't said something or if she hadn't been going to the airport with me, I would have hit the cow.

Something happened after that I found significant. I was sitting on the airplane waiting for my flight to take off and the phone rang. It was my wife and she said, "Hi."

I said, "Thanks for the ride."

She said, "Great. Have a good flight." She said, "By the way, I took a different route home."

I said, "Really? Why is that?"

She said, ""I was listening to the radio on the drive back from the airport and they said there was a wreck – a big truck had run into a cow on Christensen Road." I felt bad and I was glad it was a big truck because I knew the driver wouldn't get hurt. I thought, that was a close call for me, wasn't it? I hadn't thought of reporting the hazard because living in the country means livestock on the road at times.

What if that had been somebody taking their child to school? By the way, how much worse would I have felt if it was one of those parents who don't buckle their child in a safety belt? What if their collision with the cow caused the child to go flying out of the window and be killed? What kind of ache in my heart would I have had for the rest of my life? Now, when I see hazards on the road I report them right away. I don't want the pain and the guilt of saying, "Hey, you should have done something, or you could have done something."

Here is an example of someone who will never have the nightmare of someone getting hurt or killed because he didn't intervene. A plant manager of a refinery, where I was doing my safety talks, gave an opening safety share that was awesome. He began by saying, "Something interesting happened yesterday." He reported, "I'm at the gas station getting gas and there was somebody standing at the pump pumping gas, smoking a cigarette." So he said, "I went over to the person and explained to him smoking while pumping gas is very hazardous and it would be better if they didn't smoke while they were pumping gas."

"At that point, the smoker told me some places I might want to go on my next vacation." I thought that was a rather elegant way of putting it. He then said, "You don't understand. There are some children in a car here and if all of a sudden that flares up, the heat from that, just the radiant heat, could burn their tender skin. God forbid if it transferred the fire to their car. We might not get them out of their car seats fast enough. That would be really tragic."

At that point, the person told him some places he could stick certain things in certain orifices of his body, at which point, the plant manager said, "Okay, fine." He walked over to the wall, where there's a switch, which all gas stations have, hit it and he turned off every pump in the gas station. Everybody looked over at him and he pointed over to the person smoking. Then they stared at him.

Now, did that person stop smoking cigarettes at gas pumps? My guess is, no. But, I can guarantee you that plant manager will never feel bad he didn't say something. He will never have the nightmare of watching flames engulf a car with children in it thinking to himself, "What if I'd said something?"

What I want people to think with regard to this is what pain you would experience if something happened and you chose not to warn someone. You can think back in your life to times when you thought, "Gee, should I?" and you didn't. If it had gone the other way, how would you have felt? I can say, "If that hadn't been a truck that hit that cow, I know my feelings about that incident would have been a whole lot more dramatic." That would have caused a lot more pain the rest of my life. So, another reason you want to watch out for people's safety is to avoid pain in your life.

The fifth reason I tell people to be on the watch for each other is that it is the right thing to do. Safety is the right thing to do. Watching out for each other is the right thing to do.

In summary, five of the many reasons we need to watch out for each other's safety are:
1. Watching out for others improves your own safety awareness.
2. People get distracted.
3. People have mental failures.
4. You will never suffer the pain of knowing you could have prevented an injury.
5. It is the right thing to do.

Chapter Seven

Reasons People Fail to Watch Out for Other People's Safety

What do you think when you see somebody doing something hazardous? Let's say I see somebody on a ladder. They're working in a hotel lobby, and they're changing a light bulb in one of the chandeliers. They put a ladder up and climb up there to change one light bulb. Then they see another one's out. They have another bulb with them, and so they think, "Oh, shoot, I can reach that." Now, they should take the ladder and move it to the other position so they can do it safely, but they're trying to save time. So they reach a little farther.

Imagine we go out into the hallway and we see somebody doing that. What do you think? What you think is that nothing is going to happen because our life's experiences tell us in most cases, nothing will happen. We have all done something similar ourselves. We've all taken short cuts when we've reached a little bit farther than we should and nothing happened. Once we believe nothing's going to happen, we cease to be concerned.

Let's change the situation and imagine for a second, you know for a fact what is going to happen. There used to be a TV show called Early Edition. The premise of the show was that this guy's cat would bring him the next day's newspaper. So he'd read headlines that would tell him what was going to happen. For example, he'd look at it and read, "At 8 o'clock, 15 school children killed at the corner of First and Main Street." The story says that an out-of-control bus runs into them. He had this special knowledge so he had to arrive there before 8 o'clock and move the kids. Then, the headline would change and they wouldn't die. That was his job. He had to prevent horrible incidents from happening.

What if you could really do that? My guess is, for any audience to which I've ever spoken, if we knew for a fact we'd see somebody on a ladder, and at that moment they would fall just right, hit their head and die, we would take action. If we knew it with certainty, if we could really predict the future, I don't believe there is a single person you or I would bump into who wouldn't go out there and do something to make a difference.

I don't know about you, but if I knew that was going to happen, I'd probably take the ladder and hide it. My position would be this guy is not going to climb up the ladder today. If it meant saving a life, I'd break the ladder. I'd saw it in half. If you knew for a fact the person was going to die, you'd intervene. You would do what it takes. The problem is you don't get to know ahead of time. What I suggest to people is, they need to think in those terms.

Let's change some of the circumstances and see what you'd do. What you do is determined by what you think. If you think the person is not going to fall, you don't do anything. But if you think he is going to fall, you intervene. I can change the context. What if my wife and I are visiting my daughter, her husband and their two kids? Lauren, my granddaughter is almost three years old. We see her start heading toward the street. What do you guess I would do?

One possibility is I could say to someone, "See Lauren over there? She's a brilliant kid, because everybody thinks their kid or their grandchildren are smarter than everybody else, right? By the way, since I'm in the safety business, I talk a lot about safety. When I'm with her. I give her little safety talks and coaching, and it's great. In fact, she's so brilliant, that when she gets within 12 inches of the curb, she will come to a stop. I taught her the street is dangerous so she will not go close to it because she knows better."

That is never going to happen, no matter what. As soon as Lauren starts heading for the street, what am I going to do? I'm going to reach out, grab her, and move her back where she's safe. I could see down the street a hundred yards in each direction and no cars were coming. Even with that observation, she's not going toward that street. I'm bringing her back where it's safe. I'm not willing to risk somebody I care that much about getting hurt.

Also, consider that people think they're indestructible. They have the belief it's not going to happen to them. I wonder how much we transfer that over to other people. Think about it for a moment. When you see somebody doing something risky, what's your natural reaction? Nothing's going to happen, and that is reinforced by your life's experiences. Nothing does happen the majority of times when people do something at risk. They don't get hurt.

If every time you took a shortcut, if every time you did something risky, you got hurt, we wouldn't need to worry about safety. People would just choose to perform tasks safely.

A great example of that was when you were a little kid and your mom said, "Don't touch the stove." What did you do? You touched the stove. What happened? You burned your hand. You know what, nobody here got up this morning, walked over to the stove, and went, "Oh, Mom's still right." You didn't touch the stove again. You got an immediate lesson that was backed up by a soon, certain, and negative consequence.

If every close call resulted in a collision, people would get a lot better at driving. People would pay a whole lot more attention. It would wake them up. But, that's not the way the world works, thank goodness. People would still get distracted and experience cognitive failure, and get hurt every time.

Talk to people who have experienced somebody getting hurt and they will tell you how quickly their concern regarding someone deepens when they get injured. They feel badly when they could have helped someone avoid an injury, but didn't. They find out they really do care about people.

I once asked an audience what their perception was of the reasons people don't always watch out for each other's safety. A typical answer is that some people look at you as if you've distracted them from accomplishing the task they wanted to finish. They might say, "Don't get in my way." Which causes someone who sees a hazard to think, "Who needs the hassle, I'm not going to say anything."

Some people can't always recognize risk. Sometimes, they don't even see the hazard. I had never thought of the last idea, which is why I ask my audience questions. It draws them into the process and I learn new ideas, as well.

What if I could show you a way to make it comfortable and also give you something you could say? Something you could share with other people. Remember, there are plenty of things you can say, but if it's not comfortable, and you're afraid you're going to get an argument from somebody, you're not going to bother.

Making something comfortable is the first step to making it something you will want to do. For me, I wanted to get fit and burn off my excess fat. I knew I had to begin to eat the way fit people do and I knew I had to move more.

The second step was the tough part for me. At 394 pounds, almost all forms of exercise are uncomfortable. I needed to find something I enjoyed doing. Riding a bicycle was the key for me, and I don't mean a stationery exercise bike. I mean one on which I can ride outdoors. Once I wanted to do it, I figured out a way to make it happen and to make it comfortable. As of this writing, I have burned off about 100 pounds with about 120 to go.

I hope by now you have enough reasons to watch out for others' safety. You just need to make it comfortable and find out how. I'm going to talk about that in communicating safety right now.

One of the reasons people don't communicate safety is they don't feel comfortable. You avoid things that are uncomfortable, right? The first time I got my bike out, I thought, "Okay! Bike riding! I might like that." I used to like bike riding. So, I bought a bike at REI. I told them, "I need a bike that'll hold someone my size." They sold me a bike that could support my starting weight. First time I got on it, what happened? You know those little bike seats that come on the bike? They don't make them for people who weigh over 300 pounds. Trust me.

So, I went to the bike store and I said, "Hey, listen, at the gym, they have big giant seats on the exercise bikes. Do you have large seats that will fit on my bike?"

They said, "Oh, yes," and they bring this seat out and it's big. I call it the Buttmaster 5000. It's huge!

When my editor, Sandie, saw it she said, "That's not a bike seat, it's a sofa."

I said, "You bet it is." It's great and it's comfortable. It made riding the bike enjoyable. I got a little different handlebar so I can sit upright because that was more pleasant for me. What if people could enjoy sharing safety with somebody? Would they be more likely to do it? What if – even if they didn't enjoy it, what if it wasn't painful? What if it wasn't uncomfortable? Would they be more likely to be involved and participate in safety? Of course they would. We need to get people to want to actively care for others

The world is moved along, not only by the mighty shoves of its heroes, but also by the aggregate of tiny pushes of each honest worker.

Helen Keller

Chapter Eight

Take Personal Responsibility – Ask Others to Watch Out for Your Safety

When companies bring me in to speak at one of their employee safety meetings, the first presentation I do is titled, "Ensure Your Safety." In that presentation, I focus on the concept of taking personal responsibility for your own safety. After all, when an injury occurs, the person injured is the one who pays the greatest price or consequence for the injury. They are the one who must endure the pain, inconvenience, disability, or rehabilitation that results from the injury. Even if the individual is not at fault, they are ultimately the one who pays for the injury. Given this, it makes sense to take personal responsibility for your own safety.

The fact that you have this book means it is likely you have taken one important step in that direction and that is you have chosen to work for a company that holds safety as a value. It is important to find a company and leadership who are committed to everyone's safety.

Even in the safest companies, however, hazards and risks can occur. When they do, it is critical you are watching out and are ready to do what it takes to protect yourself and others. Following safety procedures and using personal protective equipment are key elements. Also, as mentioned earlier, taking on the task of watching out for the safety of others improves your own safety.

Watching out for the safety of others begins with taking personal responsibility. Begin by making sure all those you work with know you want them to watch out for your safety. Let them know one-on-one, if they see you near a hazard, you always want them to point it out to you. You might want to share with them some of the reasons why it is important, such as being distracted or having a cognitive failure. By asking them to watch out for your safety, you are making it comfortable for them to point out a hazard when they see one near you. Also, by asking others to watch out for your safety, you have set in motion making actively caring for others the cultural norm. Your work site will be safer when more people ask others to watch out for their safety.

Also, remind them if they notice you doing less than the safest behavior, you would appreciate their input and would like them to point it out to you. Every one of us can have a day when we aren't at our best. I have heard numerous stories over my career of people who were known for their great safety performance who let their guard down only once and that was the time they were injured. Let your fellow workers know you want them there for you all the time.

Remember, also, how you respond to them when you ask for their input is going to determine whether or not they believe you really want the input. When someone points something out to you please make it a point to profusely thank them. The more you make them realize you appreciate it, the more likely they will do the same favor for you and others in the future. Once again, it isn't always about you — it can make a difference to the safety of everyone at your operation.

For me, a change in how I wanted input from others started at home not at work. It was not uncommon for my wife and me to be driving together on the freeways of California. When she noticed a hazard such as brake lights ahead she would let me know. I used to respond by telling her I saw them and I knew what I was doing. This wasn't the best way to handle the situation from a safety or a relationship point of view. After a few years in this business, I began to realize how valuable her paying attention was to my safety. I have now changed the way I react to her feedback.

Now, when she points out a hazard such as brake lights ahead, I thank her for letting me know and I would appreciate it if she kept doing so. My ego is still involved so I do let her know when I had also seen them and I let her know I still want her input. Thanking her often increases her awareness and input and it improves our relationship.

One other thought comes to mind. You should ask all the people around you, regardless of their position or title. Whether you're the newest person on the job or the most experienced person, you still need everyone else's input. You could be a part-time employee or the owner of the business. Injuries do not respect or recognize rank or position. Make sure you have asked everyone to watch out for your safety.

Do not wait for leaders; do it alone, person-to-person.

Mother Teresa

Chapter Nine

How to Share Safety with Others

What a great place you are in. You are motivated and now you have a good enough reason why you would want to watch out for the safety of others. You have already taken the first step of asking others to watch out for your safety and now, you are ready to learn how to share safety with others in a way that is comfortable for you and them.

So, what do you do when you see an unsafe act happening or you see someone near a hazard? What do you say that feels comfortable? I remember several years ago, observing these two ladies in my neighborhood. It was before I started riding a bike, and I noticed them doing something for their fitness that was outstanding. They would walk every single day in the country near where I live and I'd think, "That's pretty good."

But while they were doing this great thing for their health, I noticed they were doing something incredibly unsafe. They were walking down the little country road with a 55 mile an hour speed limit, yellow line down the middle, and they're walking on both sides of the road. Someday, I might be driving down the road and I have trouble with my car, causing me to swerve. In which case, I'm going to hit one of them. I would have to decide which one would live.

One day, I'm at the end of my driveway and I see them about a hundred yards away walking in my direction. I think to myself, gee, I wonder if I should say something. What will they think? I think to myself that I speak to people like you all the time and tell them why they should care enough to say something, so I'd better do what I teach people. It is important to be congruent and if you stand in front of groups and tell people to talk to others about safety and then you don't do it yourself, that's not going to work. So I thought, "Okay, I'm going to tell them."

I wait until they arrive at my mailbox and I proceed to say, "I see you ladies walking every day. I really admire that and it's great for your health, but I notice you do something that's very risky. You're walking on either side of the street and if someone had to swerve, one of you is going to die."

They responded by saying, "We hadn't thought of that."

I then added, "You might want to walk on the side of the road facing traffic since there is no sidewalk here. Then, if you notice a car coming at you, at the very least, you could jump out of the way. If the driver had to take an emergency action, they could swerve the other way to avoid hitting either one of you."

They thanked me for pointing that idea out to them. They made a big deal of praising me for what I did. They said, "We really appreciate it. We saw you standing there and were wondering what you were waiting for. Not many people would take the time or care enough to do that. Thank you for doing that, and thank you for caring."

The reason I'm telling you about all the praise they gave and how much they appreciated me is not to tell you what a great guy I am. I tell you because of what happened next. I got in my car, and I started to drive away. The first thought that popped into my head as I make the turn was, "I wonder if they think I'm a jerk." Where did that come from? They just told me how much they appreciated my intervention.

I can tell you where that thought came from. It was the result of my asking the wrong question. Remember, while I was standing at the mailbox, the question I asked myself was, "What will they think?" Your brain is an amazing computer and it is capable of doing some amazing stuff.

The speed at which it works is incredible. Long before computers could do multiple tasks at the same time, the human brain was created to do just that.

When I stood there by the mailbox and saw them coming, I asked a question that put my mind into search mode. I was searching for all the possible things the ladies might have thought. I had asked myself the wrong question. Instead of random speculation in my own mind, I would have been better off asking them what they wanted me to do. Your brain will give you the answers to the questions you ask. Therefore, it is really important to focus on asking the right questions.

I asked the question, "What will they think?" There are a lot of possible answers to that question. It turns out the first one that popped into my consciousness was, "Do they think I'm a jerk?" That answer will make anyone feel bad. It fascinates me that even with their positive response, my mind thinking of this possible answer let me feel discouraged.

A couple of weeks later, in Rock Springs, Wyoming, I was doing a presentation in a college lecture hall. I had a man up on stage and I noticed his shoelace was untied. When the trick was finished, he needed to go up the stairs to return to his seat. If he stepped on his shoelace going up the stairs, he would trip and fall, hurting himself. You have heard you should correct people in private. I didn't have that option. At that moment, I thought of what to say. I turned to him and said, "Would you like me to watch out for your safety?"

He said, "What?"

I again said, "Would you like me to watch out for your safety?"

He said, "Sure." I then told him about his loose shoelace.

When you ask that question, people are going to wonder what you are referring to and will probably start looking around. They know you've got something in mind and are naturally curious, which is why this question will almost always result in a "yes" answer.

Significantly, nothing negative popped in my head. Why? This time I asked a better question. Instead of asking myself, "What will he think? I asked him, "Do you want me to watch out for your safety?" He answered and I did not have to speculate. I knew what he wanted because he told me.

Afterwards, somebody asked me what would you have done if he had said no? Simple. I can always use a new safety story. I'd have stepped on his shoelace and tripped him. Well, it would have been safer to fall on the flat stage, don't you think?

Just kidding, but seriously, I asked the man a question. Would you like me to watch out for your safety? What if somebody says no? As rare as that is, I probably would have told him anyway, but I have to tell you a no answer to that question would be unlikely.

So, what if someone does respond negatively? How can you handle that in an effective way? I was speaking at ExxonMobil and a lady came up to me afterwards and said, "What do you do if somebody does say something negative?" She said her neighbor is always mowing the lawn without wearing shoes. She really wants to say something to them but was concerned as to how they would react. Once again, the best approach is to simply ask, "Would you like me to watch out for your safety?" But, what if they did react negatively? I find a good way to deal with this issue is to think ahead of time what you would say.

What if somebody says, "Hey, would you get out of here. I need to get this job finished. What do you think I am, stupid?"

What if they did this? What would I do? I'll tell you the strategy I've developed that works for me. What I do is think to myself, that person is probably having a bad day. It's not about me; it's about them at that moment. I am willing to be forgiving and if I have thought about this reaction ahead of time, I am less likely to be caught off guard. After all, I know there are days when I've had a bad day. I mean, we've all had days when everything seems to go wrong.

Think of a time when things weren't going right for you. Things are not working the way you want in the world. Have you ever gotten off the phone with somebody and it was not the phone call you wanted to have — things are going badly, you're irritated, and you're angry? Then some person you care about walks in the room and they innocently say, "Hi." You bark at them. It wasn't them, was it? It was the state you were in and you were having a bad moment.

If I point out to somebody, "Hey, would you like me to watch out for your safety here?" and they bark at me, I think, wow, maybe they're having a bad day. I can cut them some slack. I'm not perfect. I have moments when I'm not my best. That's okay. I'll let them yell at me. By the way, it's okay anyway. I know they're not going to get hurt because I said something. I did something to make a difference. If they choose not to pay attention to it, that's a choice they're making. I know for myself, I've done all I can do.

I set that up in my mind ahead of time in case it happens. By the way, it doesn't happen all that often. It really doesn't. Once again, if you ask them the right way, "Hey, would you like me to watch out for your safety?" most of the time, people appreciate your advice. They are almost certain to say 'yes' because they are at the very least curious. So, most of the time they're going to say 'yes' at which point you tell them. You're not going to feel bad about it because they're going to be okay with your help. So ask the question. Instead of saying, "What will they think," I say, "Do you want me to watch out for your safety?" and when they say, yes, I have permission to actively care.

On the lighter side, there is something else you could do if somebody does bark back at you. Ask them to hold on for a moment while you go get your video camera. Let them know you want to put it on YouTube with all the other funny safety videos.

It is good to have more than one way to get something done. That is true in communicating safety.

Another way to share safety with someone is to use the simple phrase, "As you know..." For example, "As you know, there's a hazard there." Or, "As you know, you need someone to help you lift something like that."

Maybe you're working with somebody who is an experienced worker, somebody who knows their job. This technique is great in that kind of situation. I have the privilege of speaking to a lot of very skilled workers. I spoke to the Labor Division of the National Safety Council at their national meeting. The people in this audience are skilled craftspeople and experts at their jobs. Before the meeting, I was talking with a friend who is dedicated to safety and has been a shop steward in the International Brotherhood of Electrical Workers for years. We were discussing how even the most qualified person can have a bad day. This phrase, "As you know..." is especially useful when you are dealing with someone whom you respect and you want to make sure they aren't injured. The statement itself acknowledges their expertise and assumes they already knew of the hazard or the correct way to accomplish the task.

This gives the person being protected a graceful response. For example, maybe someone saw me lifting a table that was a little too heavy for one person to lift. They could walk over and say, "John, as you know, you need someone to help you lift that table." I could easily respond, "I knew that. I was just coming to get you." Both of us could pretend I knew what I was doing whether I did or not.

Many of you know I am a big fan of the space program. For years, NASA has been one of my clients. The cover of my book, "Mastering Safety Communication" has a picture of me sitting on board the space shuttle Atlantis. I've been on board three of the space shuttles. When I have spoken at NASA facilities, they always take me around to see the work they do. When I visit their different operations, I watch the people work. These are skilled technicians who are the best at what they do.

One day, we were watching contractors put together pyrotechnics that makes some of the orbiters' systems work. The item they were installing was a NASA standard initiator, which fires off the explosive bolts and other devices. There are three people who make sure this process goes perfectly. They understand the possibility of human error and failure and they also understand there is zero tolerance for error.

Walter Cronkite, at the launch of the Moon mission, said that even if you had a 99.9 percent quality rating for the rocket we launched to fly to the Moon, with only .01 percentage part failure, you'd still have over 2000 parts that would critically impact the mission. When he was talking about critically impacting the mission, it means loss of crew and spacecraft. There's no room for error. Yet, they understand it's possible for incredibly skilled people to have something go wrong.

One technician takes a device, puts wires through it and twists, turns it a certain number of turns and into the explosive bolt it goes. Then he takes a retaining wire that makes sure it can't unscrew, twists it a certain number of times, and then hands it to a second technician. The second person counts the number of twists, and checks each of the bolts to see that the wire went through properly.

Finally, they hand it to a NASA inspector who then checks what the other two people did. If something isn't right and it fails, people die. But, the first technician who performed the task isn't upset the other people are checking his work because he understands. He's human and humans make mistakes. Things can go wrong.

So, when I'm doing something and you care enough to say to me, "John, as you know, there's a hazard there." I need to think, "Hey, that person cares about me." I can say, "Thanks for watching out for me."

There are times when you need to intervene very quickly. That happened during a break when I was doing a seminar. I was standing at the front of the room, near the center aisle, when two hotel employees were calling out for us to get out of the way. They were moving the coffee service table to the back of the room. I didn't realize that, so I actually stepped right into their path. Then I realized what they were doing and saw more people in the aisle they could collide with because they were moving so quickly.

I raised my hand and said, "Stop, please set the table down." Then I said, "Let me help you out. Where are you moving this table?" They told me and then I announced to the room we needed the aisle clear and they would be coming through to the back of the room. I thanked them for stopping and said I just didn't want to see them or anyone else get injured. They thanked me and on they went. Sometimes, you have to act quickly and you can add the helpful language after the fact.

Chapter Ten

How to Respond When Someone Watches Out for Your Safety

When you want to improve your safety culture, teaching people how to respond when someone watches out for them is critically important. I got an outstanding view of this when I was performing a trick where a dollar bill from an audience member is destroyed and then ends up restored inside a lemon. To finish this trick, I borrow a knife from someone in the audience and cut the lemon in half. One day, after doing this trick, a gentleman walked up to me afterwards and said, "John would you like me to watch out for your safety?" I said, "Sure." He then said, "When you cut the lemon in half it would be much safer if you had gloves on. Would you like a pair of leather gloves that are Kevlar-lined?" I said, "That would be great." He went and got me a pair and I started using them during my next presentation. I was now safer because he watched out for my safety and I thanked him for that.

A couple weeks later, I was doing the same trick and another gentleman came up to me afterwards and said, "John would you like me to watch out for your safety?" I said, "You bet." He said, "I noticed when you are cutting the lemon you wore leather gloves and those are good. We have gloves that are Kevlar and are more cut-resistant than leather. You could cut through the leather with a sharp knife."

At that point, he's watching out for my safety and protecting me. How I respond to his concern goes beyond protecting just me. It can impact other people this gentleman observes in the future. How I respond has everything to do with whether he will choose to help others in the future. Remember, the gentleman was telling me about the Kevlar cut-resistant gloves and recall also that the leather gloves I was using were Kevlar-lined. No one knew that except me. I could have said to him, "Oh, hey, don't sweat it, these have a Kevlar lining."

What effect would that response have on the second gentleman in our story? One possibility is he might have felt I was putting him down because he didn't know. He might have felt foolish he didn't realize I would have had the best gloves. He was trying to help me so it was important for me to let him do so. Otherwise, he could have walked away thinking he shouldn't have said anything. I would have made him feel uncomfortable about watching out for other people's safety. If I made him feel uncomfortable, he might choose not to help the next person he sees doing something more hazardous. His internal dialogue might be, "Should I say something? No, I got beaten up the last time I tried to help." He fails to say anything and someone gets injured.

Once the hazard's been pointed out to me, how I respond is not about me; it's about the next person. So, I said to him, "Hey, that's great." He went to get me a pair and they are the ones I use now. To this day, he believes he helped me out and he did. So did the other guy. The secret to the interaction I had with the second person is I didn't steal his moment of helping from him. That moment is about him and the next person he's going to help.

Whenever somebody points out safety to you, please do whatever you can to make it a big a deal. Say, "Thanks very much, I really appreciate that. Thank you for actively caring!" This response will generate the continued behavior of watching out for others' safety.

Chapter Eleven

Sharing Safety with Your Family and Friends

Many companies talk about safety on the job. It is obvious they want to make sure no one gets hurt doing their job. My clients have learned that safety off the job is as important as safety on the job. When people integrate safe thinking and behavior into their day-to-day activities both on and off the job, their focus and ability to observe hazards and risky behaviors are constantly sharpened. Another reason I like that my clients want people to be safe off the job, is that it is an indicator their leadership is truly interested in people's safety. It's not just about the dollars it costs when someone is hurt on the job.

I actually would love to see companies use their belief in safety as a value as a recruiting tool. After all, I want my children working for a company that teaches them the importance of safety. That way, they and my grandchildren are going to be less likely to be injured.

That brings us to the topic of this final chapter — sharing safety with your family and friends. A great place to start is for you to ask your family members and friends to watch out for your safety. It gives them a reason to increase their own safety awareness. You can even show them your focus on safety if you get more specific. You could ask family and friends to watch out for your safety when you are: mowing the lawn, using a leaf blower, climbing a ladder, working with power tools, or doing other tasks around the house. Think of how often you are reaching for things, getting out of a car, or multi-tasking while doing a household activity. In these situations, having someone watch out for you could make a difference. You could teach the children how to do the dishes and include a few tips about knife safety. Keep it natural, simple and fun.

Your family and friends learn what your values are and what is important to you by listening. They hear what you talk about most. My family knows my relationship with God is very important to me because it is something we talk about on a regular basis. Ask yourself what your family and friends hear you talking about. It can be a very enlightening exercise. When they hear you talk about safety they learn how important it is to you and that will help make it important to them.

When you are going places and doing things with your family, use these as natural opportunities to discuss safety. Some recreational topics could be swimming, boating, hunting, fishing, skiing, camping, hiking, the list goes on.

My wife, Karen, and I went camping with our daughter, Jessica, her husband, Paul, and our grandchildren, Lauren and Owen. They rented a boat and we went out fishing. We made it a big deal that Lauren and Owen got to wear a life jacket just like Mom and Dad and Grandpa. They learned from the start what are the best safety behaviors.

All of the above items can be discussed in the context of helping you to be safe. I can assure you every kid out there wants their Mom and Dad to be safe because they want them to come home every day.

Make everyday activities into an opportunity to discuss safety as it applies to you and your family. Safety becomes one of those natural learning conversations you can have anywhere. While you are driving, you can discuss the importance of checking your mirrors, watching your speed, using hands-free cell phones, pulling off the road to text, taking a break on long drives to keep alert.

Nothing can substitute for professional driver training. Yet, I believe the best driver training you can give your kids is the example of outstanding safe driving practices for 16 years before they get their license. They get real-life situations they can relate to because they were there. You can point out kids on bikes and why they are hard to see. Driving down the street they may see a dog and you can point out how important it is to go slowly in a residential district because kids and dogs don't understand cars and traffic and might step out suddenly chasing a ball or running to see a friend.

As you know, when people know the reason why they should be doing something a certain way, they are more likely to do it. There are many everyday opportunities to share the why of what you do to live safely.

One of the things I love about doing magic in my safety presentations is I know people go home and tell their friends and family all about the tricks they saw at the safety meeting. This is powerful on several levels. First, it lets the friends and family know you were at a safety meeting. It also makes the meeting and the content of my presentation memorable to the audience. From the discussion of one of the magic tricks, you could share some of the safety principles you learned.

Many of my audience members ask where they can buy some magic tricks for their family or to use in their safety meetings. You can go to my website and order a great magic kit which has about 20 to 30 minutes of magic tricks included. We sell it for about 30% less than it would cost you to get it at a regular magic store or online. Also, included is an instructional DVD on which I show you how all the tricks are performed. If you are interested, go to www.drebinger.com and check it out.

Thank you in advance for your focus on the safety of others. Not only will you improve and protect the lives of the ones you love, you will also help protect people you may never meet. Enjoy sharing safety with your family, friends, co-workers and people you meet every day.

You Made it To The End!
If you started at Chapter Six and enjoyed what you learned, I encourage you to read the first five chapters to see how you can teach the same material using a story. I encourage you to read the whole book again. As a fellow author once said to me, "It takes an author sometimes a year to write a book and then weeks of editing and rewriting to focus each and every idea. It would be unwise to think any reader would be able to absorb all the concepts in just one reading."

I also have several books I read every few years. The reason for this is something I learned reading the Bible. I noticed, as have others I have studied with, you can read a book or chapter from the Bible and see, hear, feel, or learn something new. Clearly, the words did not change on the page, so what happened? It is because you have changed or your life situation is different than the first time you read it. Your viewpoint is different so what you learn can be different, also. In my recommended reading section are some books you might enjoy. If I can be of further service, please call my office at (209) 745-9419.

Recommended Reading List

Bacon, Jack. (2001). My Grandfather's Clock. Normandy House. Houston, TX 77259-1066. Phone: 866-447-4622. www.drjackbacon.com

Bacon, Jack. (2006). The Parallel Bang. Normandy House. Houston, TX 77259-1066. Phone: 866-447-4622. www.drjackbacon.com

Carnegie, Dale. (1936). How to Win Friends and Influence People. Simon & Schuster. New York, NY 10010.

Cernan, Eugene, & Davis, Don. (1999). The Last Man on the Moon. St. Martin's Press. New York, NY

Chaikin, Andrew. (1994). A Man on the Moon. Penguin Books. New York, NY

Drebinger, John. (1997). Mastering Safety Communication. Wulamoc Publishing. Galt, CA 95632. Phone: 209-745-9419. www.drebinger.com

Drebinger, John, & Deuel, Darrel. (2005). Changing The World – Finding Your Place in the Great Commission. Wulamoc Publishing. Galt, CA 95632. Phone: 209-745-9419. www.drebinger.com

Geller, E. Scott. (1996). Working Safe. Chilton Book Company. Radnor, PA

Geller, E. Scott. (2002). The Participation Factor. American Society of Safety Engineers. IL

Geller, E. Scott. (2005). People-Based Safety: The Source. Coastal Training Technologies Corp.

Geller, E. Scott. (2008). Leading People-Based Safety - Enriching Your Culture. Coastal Training Technologies Corp.

Geller, E. Scott, & Veazie, Bob. (2008). The Courage Factor: Leading People-Based ™ Culture Change. Coastal Training Technologies Corp.

Geller, E. Scott, Veazie, Bob, & Wills, George. (2010). When No One's Watching: Living and Leading Self-Motivation.

The Holy Bible. New International Version. (1984). International Bible Society. Zondervan Publishing.

Poynter, Dan. (1985). Is There A Book Inside You? Para Publishing. Santa Barbara, CA www.parapublishing.com.

Poynter, Dan. (2002). The Self-Publishing Manual. Para Publishing. Santa Barbara, CA www.parapublishing.com

Acknowledgements

One of the special privileges of writing a book is that you get to publicly thank people who have had a profound effect on your life. This is where I get to thank some of the people who have helped me on my journey. For the average reader, these people may be unknown, but I wish you had the opportunity to enjoy the pleasure of knowing them as I have over the years.

First, I am grateful to God for the direction He has given me in life and to the outstanding model teacher, Jesus, who in addition to giving his life for me also showed the world and me how to teach and communicate most effectively. Pastors of the churches I have attended over the years, Fred Doty, Robert Blacka, Luther Tolo, Vern Holmes, Charlie Knorr, Scott Minke, Tim Stevenson, Darrel Deuel, Richard Eddy, Robert Salge, Len Brokenshire, Steve Lundblom, Hassar Omega, and Jamie Eisenbeisz, trainer at The Sending Place. Their teachings have planted many seeds, which have developed into the ideas I share.

Next, I am thankful for my Mom and Dad, Bernadette and John Drebinger, for giving me life and always being there to help and guide me. They were wonderful parents and we had many amazing times together.

I am indebted to my wonderful wife, Karen, who has stood beside me for the past 40 years of marriage and always been there when I needed her. She is the one who did what it took for me to pursue a career in magic, which led to my becoming a professional speaker. Because of her trust, I have a career I love and enjoy.

I appreciate my children, Jessica and Johnny, for being the best kids I could have ever hoped for. I am thankful for my grandchildren, Lauren and Owen, who remind me every day that my job is to get parents safely home to their little ones who are counting on them.

I especially want to thank Diane Weiss for her dedicated calling day after day that places me in front of more and more audiences. There are families who can thank her for getting their loved ones home safely because they heard and acted upon my message.

I am grateful for Sandie Gilbert, my editor, who on many occasions worked late into the night in order to make me appear to be literate. Knowing she will edit my work makes it easier for me to write and create. She also directs my Dynamic Presentations Institute.

I am thankful for my peer reviewers, Jack Bacon, Cliff Butler, J. T. Cocke, Phillip Combest, Pat Gagliardi, Scott Geller, Pam Graviet, Harold Hobbs, Fred Hrenchir, Frank Malquist, Don Melanson, Nancy Moorhouse, Alan Rosen, Powell Stevenson, and Mack Wimbish. They gave of their time to make sure the book you have read is the best it can be.

Last, but not least, I would like to recognize every person out there who actively cares about their safety and the safety of others. You are literally changing the world every day by what you do and say. For that reason, I have left a special place for your name in my book. Please fill in the blank space below with your name because without you taking actions on what you have just learned, this book is just words. You bring it to life.

I would especially like to thank _____ for actively watching out for the safety of others.

Yours in Service,
John Drebinger Jr.

John W. Drebinger Jr., CSP, CHt.

For over 20 years, John Drebinger has worked with companies that want an injury-free workplace and helps people embrace safety as a value. He motivates people to take personal responsibility for their own safety. His audiences take action on what they learn from him. His presentations are always fun and effective. John serves a diverse list of clients including NASA, ExxonMobil, General Motors, Bechtel, The U.S. Military, Dow Corning, Boeing, 3M, Chevron, and many others. John helps leaders communicate safety messages that deliver results. John has a Bachelor's Degree in Speech and is a Certified Hypnotherapist. He has earned the National Speakers Association's highest earned designation, "Certified Speaking Professional." John is a Professional Member of the American Society of Safety Engineers, a member of the famous Hollywood Magic Castle and an Eagle Scout.

Contact: John Drebinger Presentations   Ph: 209-745-9419
13541 Christensen Rd., Galt, CA 95632
Email: john@drebinger.com   Website: www.drebinger .com

Discover the Magic of Great Safety Presentations

John Drebinger is unique in the world of professional safety speakers. Unlike many safety speakers who have only one presentation, John's difference is that he is a writer and creator of new safety material. He has helped other speakers write and improve their material. His over 20 years of experience in the safety profession have given him new and customized material all the time. So many of John's clients are impressed with the results he gets, they have had him back over and over again. He always brings an entirely new message, which he blends into their theme or slogan.

This book accompanies his presentation entitled, **"Would You Watch Out for My Safety?"**© That presentation gives people the reasons why they would <u>want</u> to watch out for the people around them and then he gives them techniques they can put into use immediately.

Some other presentation titles are:
"Ensure Your Safety" – Inspires people to take personal responsibility for their own safety.

"Safety For Leaders" – Showing leaders how to effectively and congruently help employees work safely every day.

"Safety As A Value" – Helping people embrace safety as a value for themselves, their families, and co-workers.

"Mastering Safety Communication" – A two hour to one day seminar in being an effective safety communicator.

"The Dynamic Presentations Institute" – A 2-day workshop teaching your people presentation and group skills.

"The Impossible Is Just An Illusion" – A keynote speech, which will magically kick off any convention or meeting.